To my darling husband Christopher, my Mum, Dad and Brother and all my family and friends who have been such a massive support to me.

Foreward

It is a truth universally acknowledged that doctors make the worst patients. This is my story as a patient through a doctor's eyes, which I have written with the hope that healthcare professionals will read it, in particular young doctors and medical students, and understand exactly what being a patient is really like and how their behaviours, no matter how small can impact massively on the people they look after. It is also a story of my own personal battles with control and learning how and when to relinquish this.

For the non-medics amongst you there is a glossary at the back of the book to hopefully help explain some of the technical terms and medical language I use.

The Other Side

California Dreaming

It's a beautiful warm Californian summer's afternoon and I'm sat alone in the garden surrounded by flowers blowing in a gentle breeze. Several bees are busily at work around me and a huge Monarch butterfly has just landed on the tub of milkweed. An idyllic setting you would think but for the fact that the peace is disturbed by my crying. I have been sobbing my heart out now for over an hour and I know they're worried about me inside, but I just can't stop. I never knew I had so many tears. My whole world has just collapsed around me and up until this point I had been doing my very best to maintain a strong public face. This is the first time I have actually let myself go and really cry. Jen had realised I needed to be alone and was keeping the boys busy in the house. I now look back on that hour as such precious 'coming to terms with it' time. Emotional space would be in short supply on our return to England.

Rewind a week. It had been an absolutely amazing trip. Chris and I had brought his Grandma over to Santa Cruz to see her daughter and meet her two new Great Grandchildren. We were combining doing the family thing with lots of fantastic sight seeing. I had started to feel unwell a few days into the trip with a niggling right sided back pain, but being your average doctor I ignored it, took some simple analgesia and ploughed on with the holiday. After all you don't come to California every day and can't let a little twinge get the better of you. Unfortunately the little twinge turned into a big twinge and then a massive twinge. I really did not want to have to consult a doctor in the States and I had probably procrastinated over my

3

symptoms far too long. My appetite had disappeared, I was vomiting and starting to think something was seriously wrong with me. Chris finds me laid on our bed in agony and says enough is enough. My stubbornness wanes and I give in.

John takes us to the local Urgent Care Centre. It is a nice, clean and quiet building despite it being a Saturday night with a friendly receptionist. Not being accustomed to the American healthcare system we could not believe the number of forms they insisted on us filling in whilst I was in agony. Then there was the demand, albeit a very polite demand for $200 before we could see anyone. We duly pay the money and wait our turn. I had been in two minds whether to tell them I am a Physician in the UK, but John being John did it for me! A bustling nurse soon appears to take us "out back". I tell her my details and a brief synopsis of my history whilst she types. She then does my observations. I have a blood pressure of 200/100 mmHg and a pulse of 120 bpm. I have never been hypertensive in my life, in fact I border on hypotension most of the time. Perhaps it is all the stress of the situation. I dutifully pee in a cup and am glad to discover I am not pregnant.

The doctor sees me after about twenty minutes of waiting. He is a middle aged man with glasses and a moustache. I give my history in more detail using medical jargon this time but I am struggling to articulate as clearly as I would normally due to the pain. He asks me some closed questions all of which I answer in the positive and he shakes his head. He quickly examines me. I am exquisitely tender in my right flank, loin and suprapubically. I also have referred pain from left iliac fossa to right. He asks what my working diagnosis is and I suggest a reasonable differential list including renal calculi and appendicitis.

"You've earned yourself a trip to the ER young lady, do not pass go, do not collect the money, although as I have been able to do absolutely nothing for you here you can have your $200 back." With that we leave and John drives us up the local hospital.

The Emergency Room is deceptively quiet for a Saturday evening. Our Emergency Departments in the UK would be heaving by now with fighters and drunks. We face the same administrative hurdles as at the Urgent Care Centre but soon I am being triaged. I remain hypertensive and tachycardic. The Physician Assistant who sees me writes some preliminary orders for labs, venous access, NPO (the American version of nil by mouth), fluids, anti-emetics and analgesia and I am curled up on a trolley in the ER soon after he has seen me. The nurse is a surfer dude. He cannulates me and takes the bloods. I am surprised to see they use exactly the same equipment as we do in the UK. We have an interesting conversation about the different roles of nurses and doctors either side of the Atlantic whilst he is stabbing me. He tells me doctors never really touch needles in the States unless it is a central line or something of the like. I explain junior doctors in the UK get lumbered with an awful lot of venepuncture and cannulation duties but that this is changing slowly with the introduction of Clinical Support Assistants and the up-skilling of nurses.

The ER doctor who sees me is podgy short man with a tangle of brunette curly hair. He refers to me constantly as "young lady". I have given my history so many times this evening I am starting to get sick of the sound of my own voice, but I dutifully repeat my story over again. It is becoming more succinct with each version. He examines me. I am still very tender almost everywhere. He suggests an ultrasound and if that is inconclusive they will proceed to a CT. I am impressed they have access to such diagnostics from the ER. If I had presented in the UK on a Saturday night I probably would have waited until Monday afternoon at the earliest for imaging.

The surfer dude returns after the doctor has finished with my drugs. He gives me some ondansetron first and then follows this with fifty micrograms of fentanyl. I have never had strong opiates or even weak opiates for that matter before. Soon after the injection I am floating on the ceiling with absolutely no pain at all. Now I am pain free it is the first time I realise actually how uncomfortable I have been over the past few days.

I am wheeled down to the Radiology department. The ultrasound technician is in her late fifties and when I apologise for being the reason she has had to come into work on a Saturday night she tells me not to worry, she is being paid a small fortune for the privilege of my company. A sign of money driven America I guess. She is not gentle at all with her ultrasound probe and when she is scanning my right side I am in agony despite the fentanyl. The only positive finding she reports to me is bilateral hydronephrosis but she cannot find the cause for this. I am really worried now.

When I arrive back in the ER the doctor is waiting to see me. He has my blood results and breaks it to me gently that my creatinine is 485. It takes a second longer than it would for me normally to piece it all together. Why would

I have developed an obstructive uropathy? He says we will go ahead with the CT but obviously intravenous contrast is out of the question with my current renal function, they will however still give rectal contrast. I cringe at the thought. He tells me I will obviously need to come into hospital and that the admitting doctor will see me when I return from CT. My mind is spinning with the differential diagnosis of obstructive uropathy. I cannot come up with a benign condition that causes bilateral problems and cancer keeps appearing at the top of my imaginary list. My pain has returned and the surfer dude nurse obliges with another fifty micrograms of fentanyl. I am soon floating again.

The CT scan is quite a surreal experience. So much has happened in such a short space of time, I am dealing with being suddenly seriously unwell in a foreign country and it all feels as if it is happening to someone else. A female technician explains what they need to do, but I cut her off mid spiel, tell her I'm a doctor and to just get on with it. I stupidly haven't taken off my bra in preparation for the scan and we have quite a battle removing it through the gown with my drip in situ. I am instructed to lie on my left side and after a quick PR exam she inserts a rectal speculum to administer the contrast. It feels strange as the warmed fluid runs into my colon. Soon I have terrible central abdominal cramping and she has to stop the infusion temporarily whilst I compose myself. I manage to complete the infusion after a few minutes and roll onto my back for the scan. I am moved through the scanner three times and obediently hold my breath as instructed. She drains much of the contrast away after the scan through the speculum then removes it. There is a conveniently positioned toilet in the scan room and I have a rush on to get there in time before the rest of the contrast pours out. I make it, just.

The admitting doctor is a pleasant fellow in his late thirties or early forties with slicked back hair. I repeat my history for what feels like the millionth time. He examines me and also does a pelvic. It is really uncomfortable and I virtually jump off the bed when he bimanually palpates my right adnexa. He tells me the CT has shown several soft tissue masses in my abdomen and pelvis, and one of these masses is encasing both ureters causing the obstruction. Oh my god, it really is cancer. Lymphoma, sarcoma, ovarian carcinoma, all the possible diagnoses are whizzing round my brain. I hide my understanding of the situation from Chris as it would cause him far too much worry before we know exactly what we are dealing with. The Urologist is going to come and see me in the morning with a view to retrograde ureteric stenting. I try and sleep but fail miserably. The nurse is a busty motherly woman and sits up comforting and reassuring me for well over an hour. I guess staffing levels must be better in the US.

The Urologist is an early bird. He looks like a very young George Clooney and is rather dashing in his scrubs. I wish he wasn't about to do unspeakably embarrassing things to me. He is a proper surgeon type though and is extremely brisk with his explanation. I have to ask if I will be sedated or anaesthetised. There is a wave of relief when he opts for the latter. Soon he is gone and the nurse brings the consent form for me to sign. As I am about to leave for theatre she asks me if I would like her to pray with me. I am slightly taken aback by the offer and politely decline. Although I do have faith, it is private and I certainly wouldn't share my beliefs with a complete stranger. The anaesthetist is young and has just finished her residency. She is obviously keen to get on with the job and already wields a syringe of midazolam in her hand. I feel much more relaxed for some benzodiazepines and the effect is almost instantaneous. I have left scrub trousers and underwear on not really thinking about what they were about to do to me; the theatre nurse points out we won't get very far in my current attire so the situation is rectified and I am undressed. The milk-like propofol is given next and as I count backwards I am soon asleep and blissfully unaware of the situation.

I do not remember waking up from the anaesthetic the first time. Chris was with me and says I was just very drowsy. When I do finally come round properly the first sensation is an overwhelmingly desperate urge to pass urine. It is really painful and takes my breath away. They put me on a bed pan but I am unable to wee in that position. I cannot understand why my hips are sore and stiff until I remember what has happened to me and how I must have been positioned for the procedure. The Urologist comes back to tell us he was successful and he has managed to place stents on both sides. The left side was more difficult and he had to do some contrast studies to confirm position. I am relieved to have been spared the discomfort and inconvenience of percutaneous nephrostomies. He is a little smug about the whole situation and it feels as though he is giving himself a virtual pat on the back for being such a great surgeon. I know however that this is only a temporary solution to my problems and there is going to follow many months of treatment. I struggle to concentrate on the conversation due to the extreme urinary symptoms. He reassures me he emptied my bladder at the end of the procedure and the pain will just be due to detrusor hyperactivity. He orders more opiate analgesia and after one hundred micrograms of fentanyl I feel a little better. They also give me oral rifampicin which is apparently supposed to help with dysuria type symptoms although I was not aware of this indication and we certainly do not use it for that in the UK. I am transferred back to the ward.

The first task on returning from theatre is to get up and wee. I am really wobbly on my feet but with the help of a nurse and HCA I manage to somehow flop onto the commode. I pass over four hundred millilitres of blood stained, bright orange with streaks of blue contrast mixed in urine. It is quite techni-coloured. I obviously did need to wee; just nobody would listen to me. The sense of relief is immediate. I am hooked up to intermittent pneumatic calf compression after my theatre trip and it is quite a rigmarole disconnecting me so I can use the toilet but Chris does a grand job. I continue to pass urine every hour and by the end of the afternoon we are up to four and a half litres. It is very strange as I had not noticed a tailing off of my urine output when I initially became ill, but I suppose a malignant obstruction develops very slowly. As I am clearly in the polyuric phase of recovering obstructive acute kidney injury and am still very drowsy from the morning's experience I ask if my intravenous fluids can be turned up to match my output. That is how I would manage this scenario in the UK; what goes in equals what comes out plus a bit. Unfortunately the doctor who saw me overnight has gone home and handed my care over to someone else. He is a tiny Afro-Caribbean man with poor English. He does not appear to understand my request to review my fluid balance and suggests the current regimen of sixteen hourly bags is adequate. I am too worn out to argue any further and turn the infusion pump up to 200 ml/hr myself, which even at this rate is a touch on the conservative side.

The following morning my creatinine has come down to 268 and I am in much better shape physically. On the wall in the my side room there is a white board where they write the date, who your nurse is, when observations have been done and discharge plans. It also has a space for patient questions. I have filled this space overnight. The questions are pouring out of me. I ask the nurse if I could see the original admitting doctor as opposed to the one who couldn't manage simple fluid balance. She isn't sure this will be possible but will ask for me anyway. I just want a doctor who I can have a sensible realistic conversation with so I am glad when the original doctor appears and I apologise for causing him any inconvenience. He doesn't seem to mind maintaining the continuity of care. We go through my questions which mostly revolve around making a tissue diagnosis before I leave the States. I feel this is important as cancer services in the UK are very much arranged around the specific site of cancer and it will be hard to slot me into the system with such a wide and varied differential diagnosis. He offers to discuss my case with the Interventional Radiologist to see if CT guided biopsy would be a viable option.

Jen, John and Grandma are visiting when he returns after his discussion with Radiology. He tells me the Radiologist has reviewed the CT and is reluctant to proceed to biopsy as he feels the images are most consistent with a diagnosis of ovarian cancer and that sticking needles into my abdomen would risk seeding the tumour further. This news hits me really hard. I have to struggle not to cry as

Grandma is in the room and I do not want her to be upset but I have just been told I probably have at least stage 3c ovarian cancer and I am fully aware the prognosis is dismal. He has kindly discussed my care with the Gynaecologists at Stanford, the nearest teaching hospital to Santa Cruz. They are keen to transfer me for an immediate laparotomy and debulking procedure. I just want to go home. I keep the true prognosis from Chris although I'm sure he will be on the Internet the moment my back is turned.

I am well enough to go home the following day. My discharge papers are completed and prescriptions faxed off to the local pharmacy. I receive a CD of all my Radiology images as a souvenir of the American healthcare experience. I cannot wait to return to the UK to my creature comforts but cannot face having to tell all.

Getting the ball rolling

I have my own agenda for this visit to the GP. It's the day after we arrived back in the UK and I cannot remember ever being this tired. I'm paying the price for a combination of jet lag and some very restless nights sleep, and of course recovering physically from acute kidney injury. I want my referral, prescription, blood card and sick note and I do not want to get into any Primary Care psychological support mumbo jumbo. I'm feeling surprisingly mentally strong about the cancer diagnosis and I just want to get the ball rolling with what we need to do to get me treated and back to a relatively normal life if possible. I have prepared copies of all the documentation from America and written a summary of the medical goings on to aid the referral writing process as the discharge summary is extremely brief. All this effort is aimed at me not having to go through it all in intricate detail with the GP.

I book myself in on the computer and take a seat in the light airy waiting room. My name soon pops up on the automated screen. His surgery is running on time. The GP is a lovely quiet middle aged man I have not met before. I tell him a shortened version of the convoluted tale using full blown medical speak. He listens well. However as predicted he soon tries to apply a psycho-social model to the consultation; I see this coming a mile off and tell him my way of coping with all this at the moment is by keeping things on a medical level. He tells me I should stop being a doctor and start thinking more like a patient. I listen but his perspective does not change my mind. I might be a patient now but I am also a doctor and that is a huge part of me that no-one can ever take away.

I ask for some low molecular weight heparin and he bravely tries to convince me this is probably not necessary. I argue my case with the eleven hour flight, large pelvic mass, recent surgery and recovering renal failure as enough risk factors to justify treatment. I do not want a DVT to complicate matters even further. He relents and prescribes it. I'm pretty good at winning arguments especially when I know I'm right! I feel slightly patronised when he asks if I am capable of giving the subcutaneous injections myself. He tries again with the psychological chat and tells me it's ok to cry and that I should be crying given the circumstances. I say this is for me to do privately and I'm not about to break down in front of a complete stranger. I think he accepts this.

He offers to do my bloods for me, but I look like a drug addict after my admission in America and my veins weren't that great to start off with. I say I'd rather find a competent medical Registrar or Haematology nurse at my work if he doesn't mind. I think he is quite pleased when he sees all the bruises. I've already had well over my allotted ten minutes anyway. He reassures me that he will be my allocated GP from now on and one other doctor at the Practice will know about my case if he is away for any reason but he will endeavour to maintain continuity of care where possible. I find this old fashioned approach to family doctoring refreshing and reassuring. So many times I will phone a surgery to enquire about a complex elderly patient with multiple problems and none of the GPs will really know the patient. I leave with my agenda achieved to await my hospital appointment.

Waiting

The clinic appointment has seemed an awful long time coming but in reality it is only ten days since the GP referred me, well within the Government two week suspected cancer waiting time. Having said that there is absolutely nothing 'suspected' about it in my case. Chris and I arrive early and after fathoming our way through the various administrative hoops find ourselves in a quiet out-patients waiting room. I had decided I wanted go into the appointment by myself and after waiting over half an hour and with a bit of gentle persuasion Chris leaves me to wait alone. His presence is making me more nervous for some reason.

There are two receptionists, one friendly woman who greeted me and put me much more at ease. The other lady I think must be covering this clinic temporarily and clearly does not want to be there. A young nervous looking girl arrives and stands at the desk for over two minutes before the second receptionist even acknowledges her presence. And then it is only to scorn her for not registering at the desk downstairs first. It's these tiny acts of either kindness or unfriendliness that completely change your experience as a patient. Several patients come and go, doctors pop in and out and I'm starting to think they've forgotten about me when the nurse calls my name.

I'm in a very anxious and fragile state by now. I've always hated waiting rooms, no matter what I'm waiting for. So it's no surprise to me that I'm hypertensive and tachycardic when she does my observations. I am weighed and dutifully provide the early morning urine specimen as requested. She then leads me into an empty consultation room and reassures me that the doctor won't be too long.

We're in the old part of the hospital and the consultation room is small. There is a circular table pushed up against the back wall with three chairs around it and a couch with a trolley next to it on which sits all the gynaecological examination paraphernalia. I sit down in the furthest corner and instinctively reach for the box of tissues which have been strategically positioned on the table. Spontaneously I start crying. My whole body is shaking. I've waited what seems such a long time for this appointment and now I'm actually here everything is just that little bit more real. I also cannot take my eyes off the trolley with all the torture implements on it. I'm petrified of pelvic examinations and I would do anything to avoid them.

The doctor enters. I thank God she's a woman. She introduces herself as the Registrar and is very gentle and kind in her manner. We go over my history. I try to pull myself together a little and give her a succinct account of what has happened so far. She then thinks aloud several different management plan options, one involves me coming back the following week for a pelvic ultrasound but I am secretly glad when she decides admission would be the best way forward to expedite things as there has already been some inherent delays. I am very grateful when she manages to pull some strings to get my case onto this week's MDT meeting. I do not think I can face anymore waiting. I hand over the scan CD from America and she seems impressed I have brought this. I am greatly relieved not to be examined; given my current mental state I think a pelvic examination would have finished me off.

Mad House

We go home to pick up some overnight things then present ourselves to the ward. It is in the old part of the hospital and seems a little chaotic, but it is an admissions unit and you would be doing well to find an admissions unit in the NHS that isn't chaotic. A welcoming blonde Sister is expecting us and we are ushered into a side room smack bang next to the nursing station. I dutifully put on my pyjamas like a good patient. An SHO comes by to complete my drug chart and I basically tell her what to write up. She seems relieved that I have done the thinking for her. The Registrar has completed the clerking proforma in clinic so I do not have to repeat my history but do find it a little strange that no-one examines me. I suppose they do things differently in Gynaecology compared to Medicine.

The Consultant pops by that evening. She is a youngish Asian lady with prissy glasses. She apologises for not having time to see me in person in clinic. I had been feeling miffed about this fact all day. In Elderly Medicine when our patients are retired doctors, out of professional courtesy the Consultant would always see them. She reiterates the plan for a pelvic ultrasound which has been booked for the following day, to await the vast array of tumour markers that have already been sent and the outcome of the MDT meeting. The plan seems reasonable to me and I go to sleep that evening reassured that things are on the right track.

The following morning I notice that MRI is written next to my name on the ward white board. At first I wonder if this is just an administrative error and it is actually meant to say ultrasound. They wouldn't have requested an MRI without talking to me first surely. I get claustrophobic sat in the back of a three door car so the thought of having an MRI is not a pleasant one. The next thing I know a porter has arrived with a wheelchair to take me for the mysterious MRI. I question if it is a mistake so we read the medical notes. A discussion between my Consultant and the Gynae-Oncology team is clearly documented the previous evening suggesting an urgent MRI abdomen and pelvis in addition to the rest of the management plan. I can see that it is a completely appropriate investigation but I'm absolutely fuming she did not bother to discuss this with me. As I have no other choice I sit myself in the chair and am wheeled off to the scanner. My heart is pounding the whole way.

I have lots of extra things to write on the safety questionnaire given recent events but cannot see that any of them will buy me a reprieve. I am right and am led through to the scanner room by a friendly technician. They position me on the table and secure two large plastic shields around my body. No escape now. The emergency buzzer is put into my right hand and I grip on it tightly. I accept the offered music but am not impressed as Amy Winehouse is piped through my head phones. The MRI tech must have been leading his own strange tribute to her as she had only recently died. I just don't like her music.

I have never been in an MRI scanner before. The table is moved into the scanner and I cannot believe how close the walls are to me. I am not the smallest person in the world, but I am not the largest either and I wonder how Chris would even fit in. As the table comes to a stop there is a fan blowing cool air onto my face. I am feeling really petrified now and shut my eyes tight. I decide I will not be opening them again until the scan is completed. I grip the buzzer and try to concentrate on my breathing which has become uncontrollably rapid and erratic; I do not seem to be able to just breathe normally no matter how hard I try. I am very aware that my abdomen is moving a lot when I do breathe and wonder if this will affect the image quality. Each of the scan sequences takes between three and six minutes. The machine whirrs into action and makes various loud clunking noises. They are unpredictable and I try not to let them make me jump. At one point the tech asks me to take really shallow fast breaths, as if I wasn't doing this already but I try harder and nearly make myself pass out. It causes some circum-oral tingling.

The whole experience takes over an hour and when they finally come back into the scanning room to fetch me out of the scanner I am a total wreck and daren't open my eyes despite their reassurances that it was all over. I have sweat so much the paper towel I am lying on is stuck to me. As I get myself off the table I feel really wobbly and if it wasn't for the offered arm I think I would have fainted. I keep telling myself its over but the internal scared feeling stays with me all day. As I'm sat waiting for the porter to collect me I wonder how older people cope with MRI scans, especially if they have some cognitive impairment. I vow to myself that I will only ever request really clinically essential scans if I ever get back to work.

Instead of being wheeled back to the ward I am then taken to the ultrasound department. I had thought by having the MRI that might have negated the need for the promised pelvic ultrasound but clearly not. The technician is a very polite professional girl and puts me at my ease despite the torture implements attached to the side of the scanning machine. I am scanned abdominally first. The jelly is cold but she is gentler than the technician in America. I have mild hydronephrosis bilaterally, which sets some alarm bells ringing in my head. I must keep a close eye on my renal function. The masses look huge and heterogeneous on the screen. I wonder why the American technician did not mention them as they are really clinically obvious even to my untrained eye.

Next the vaginal scan. After emptying my bladder I remove my pyjama bottoms and climb under the sheet onto a wedge shaped cushion. It takes a bit of adjusting to get comfortable and positioned correctly. I feel really awkward but lie back and try to relax. She asks me to take a deep breath and inserts the probe in one swift deliberate movement. It's cold but isn't painful. The scan takes about fifteen minutes. I think she is worried she is hurting me, she isn't, it is just a touch uncomfortable and embarrassing. When she's finished I'm bleeding a little but have survived relatively unscathed.

When I get back to the ward I am curious to know my blood results for that day given the hydronephrosis, the doctors are ever elusive so I ask a nurse to look for me. She cannot find them on the server so I look for myself knowing exactly how to manipulate the Leeds results server from all those years working in the Trust. My creatinine is 100 which is a relief. The MRI result is also there but I resist the urge to look. The Radiologists have reported it in unbelievably quick time; we would have waited a week for a report in my old hospital. Later that evening I can hear every word of the nurse's handover even with my door shut and the radio on. They refer to me as bed 27 and the Sister questions the need for me to be an in-patient as I appear so well. She clearly does not understand my case very well and is not able to predict what is about to happen.

How not to break bad news

The third day of admission brings me some examples of doctor's communication skills being the worst I could possibly imagine under the most painful of circumstances. First thing today I have been crying. It is the day of the MDT meeting, I am frightened and it feels as though nobody is talking to me. I know my MRI report is available, but again no-one has taken the time to discuss this with me so I know it must be bad news.

I'm laid in a hospital bed sobbing and scared, about at the most vulnerable a patient could be. A middle aged woman breezes into my room without knocking and announces her unpronounceable name, which I have no hope of remembering as she does not wear a name badge. She says she is a Gynaecology Registrar and has been assigned presenting my case at the MDT meeting. I think this strange as I have never met her before but continuity of care has already been sadly lacking since my admission. She continues to ask me inane questions in broken English, which make me think she has not even read my medical notes. I am really not in the mood to repeat myself yet again so am polite but relatively short with her in my manner.

She then says something that I still cannot fully comprehend to this day. She asks me why I am upset to which I respond "because I'm 29 years old and I've got cancer". Her astonishing reply to my frank yet accurate answer is "do not be silly, this won't turn out to be cancer, you are too young, it will be something benign". With that I ask her to leave. I might not be an Oncologist but I've seen my CT images in the US showing the huge lobulated pelvic mass, the distant sizeable omental mass in my left upper quadrant and the extensive lymphadenopathy. There is absolutely no doubt in my mind that this is cancer, we might not know exactly histologically what type of cancer yet, but it can't really be anything else but cancer. And to have a perfect stranger come and tell me otherwise when she cannot even take the time to read my medical notes prior to seeing me makes me furious. So furious I stop crying.

Later that morning a young Gynaecology SHO I have never met enters my room clutching my notes folder to which is clipped a long winded MRI report and a yellow Radiology request form. I can tell he has pulled the short straw and been sent to talk to the scary 'med reg'. He nervously sits down next to me and out of the blue after a cursory introduction tells me "your MRI shows evidence of spread". I am quite astounded at the lack of quality communication given the circumstances.

As an Elderly Medicine Registrar I pride myself on my abilities to break bad news well and have difficult conversations with patients and their families under the most challenging of circumstances. It is what we do and I find it one of the most rewarding and fulfilling aspects of the job. If I was tackling this communication scenario I would first prepare the ground by arranging for a relative or friend to be present if the patient wanted, make sure a nurse was with me and have the statutory box of tissues available. I would introduce myself and explore the baseline knowledge and concerns of the patient. I would then fire my warning shot, for my case it could be "your MRI results are more worrying than we first thought". This is so important to make sure the patient is really listening to you and preparing them for what is about to come.

Then I would go through the information slowly in bite sized chunks making sure they understood along the way. Finally I would offer the opportunity to ask questions and make myself available if they wanted to talk again later once the news had sunk in.

Unfortunately the communication skills I am exposed to that morning do not live up to my own standards. I am so shocked at his first sentence I ask to have the report to read for myself. I never enjoyed reading MRI reports at the best of times, they are always so long winded and use anatomical descriptions long assigned to my distant memory banks after first year anatomy classes. As I read all the words seem to mingle into one with bad phrases popping out at me along the way, "extensive lymphadenopathy", "numerous liver metastases", "sacral bone involvement". Metastatic cancer, I'm 29 years old and I've got metastatic cancer. The tears are properly flowing now and I've quite forgotten about the poor SHO sitting in the corner not knowing what to do or say. But he suddenly pipes up "they discussed your case at the MDT and they think it's a germ cell tumour, which should be very treatable". That sentence probably exceeds both his and my knowledge on the subject and with that I ask him to leave me alone. As he exits I roll over with my back to the door and let myself go.

Later that evening the Gynae-Oncology team send one of their Clinical Nurse Specialists to see me to discuss the outcome of the MDT meeting. I would have preferred to see a Consultant. She is a motherly character from the North-East and at first attempts to treat me like any other patient. I cringe at her layman description of chemotherapy and have to admit to feeling patronised. I very nearly became a Haematologist so I should know the basics of chemotherapy pharmacology. We talk about the treatment of metastatic ovarian cancer although the conversation is meaningless without my histology report. She promises I will see one of the medical Gynae-Oncologists the following day to discuss everything in more detail.

Listen

The next morning I wake up in terrible pain, exactly the same pain I had experienced in America. The first thing that springs to my mind is that my stents have failed and that I am potentially very unwell again with obstructive uropathy, not an unreasonable summation given my medical history. It is a real excruciating pain so I don't think I'm somatising. I press my buzzer for the first time since being admitted. A student nurse pops her head around the door to see me writhing around the bed complaining of ten out of ten pain. It must have been quite a shock for the poor girl who immediately leaves to get a staff nurse.

The nurse appears grudgingly ten minutes later, I explain my symptoms and ask to see a doctor as soon as possible. She mutters something about not wanting to give me the appropriately prescribed Oramorph as she does not want to mask my symptoms until I have seen a doctor. I then lie in agony for what feels like a very long two hours before she finally reluctantly relents and gives me the Oramorph. I am made to feel like an opiate seeker, which given the circumstances I don't think very fair. I soon enter the floaty, dizzy opiated state, but at least the pain is better.

It is another hour and a half before I see a doctor, who is yet again a new face who does not know me or my case. She attempts to listen to my history, makes a vague, non-systematic attempt at clinical examination without palpating my abdomen or objectively assessing my fluid status and then says she thinks I should have some intravenous fluids and we should wait for the ultrasound guided biopsy, which is planned for the next day. This management plan is not exactly what I had in mind. I know

I need urgent bloods, renal ultrasound, discussion with Urology and probably nephrostomies. The longer it takes for those things to happen the more nephrons I will lose risking permanent renal damage. I manage to convince the clearly inexperienced and unsure of herself SHO that doing some bloods might be a good idea, but I do not seem to be able to articulate to her that I've got an obstructive uropathy that needs urgent attention. Maybe it is because I am opiated or maybe it is just too much hassle for her to listen to me.

Luckily a friend who also happens to be an Elderly Medicine Consultant at the hospital pops by to visit in the midst of all these shenanigans and after seeing my distress gets involved, making sure the more senior doctors are aware of my clinical situation and before I know it I am being wheeled off for an urgent ultrasound. It's a good job as my creatinine comes back at 360 that day having been normal two days previously.

The torture chamber

I had moved to the specialist cancer centre the previous evening and was amazed at the difference in the quality of both medical and nursing care. A lovely Medical Oncology Consultant had seen me and actually examined me properly from head to toe, the first time anyone had bothered since admission. He reassured me an urgent nephrostomy had been arranged for the following day. I had brought up resuscitation during this consultation. Now I knew I had metastatic cancer the decision was easy and I definitely wanted a DNAR form. I have seen far too many people die horrible, undignified deaths in hospital where prolonged resuscitation attempts can be so messy and unpleasant just because a difficult conversation had not happened. I really do not want this to happen to me if I'm going to die anyway. He appeared taken aback that I would bring up such an emotive topic so soon into my illness but agreed to sign the form and praised me for my courage. This discussion brought me a sense of relief; it had been praying on my mind since I found out about the metastatic nature of my disease. He also discussed my analgesia with the on-call Palliative Medicine Consultant. As a result I was feeling much more comfortable both physically and mentally especially as the new nursing staff seemed to have a good understanding of the concept of breakthrough analgesia unlike the previous ward.

A porter arrives with a trolley this morning and although I am a bit woozy and wobbly with all the opiates, I am determined to get myself onto it without any help. My fierce independent spirit is not about to desert me just because I've got cancer and acute kidney injury. I have never really thought about what patients are feeling when they are being pushed around the hospital for various tests and procedures before I got ill. I find it an uncomfortable experience, especially today, watching the ceiling lights flash by, turning my head away from people I recognise and wondering how much it is going to hurt. Unfortunately my only direct clinical experience of nephrostomies was watching an old stoical chap have one done when I was a student. It had turned out to be a technically difficult procedure which the patient had really not tolerated very well at all. I think about him as I am wheeled through the corridors. This is not the first time that I wish I could erase some of my knowledge and experience of Medicine.

A lovely healthcare assistant welcomes me to the Interventional Radiology room, which I have now renamed the torture chamber. It is cold and I start to shiver. Remarks are made about my hypertension. I am really not surprised I am hypertensive given my levels of anxiety and the huge quantities of catecholamines circulating in my bloodstream at this point in time. A Radiology Registrar comes in and although I'm all for training I hope all my hope possible that a Consultant will be performing the procedures. Luckily my prayers are answered when the Consultant appears and introduces himself. A short, serious man but he has a sympathetic nature and an air of confidence that is reassuring. First there is the consent form. It is all explained at my level. He warns me that in a tiny percentage of patients having nephrostomies there is a possibility of losing the kidney. I didn't realise this and it freaks me out a little. If I lose a kidney I really would be up the proverbial creek without a paddle. I wonder to myself if he tells all the patients he performs nephrostomies on this fact or if it has been shared because I am doctor. I am asked if I am happy to proceed. To this rhetorical question I reply "I don't really have a lot of choice, do I? So crack on". The form is signed, no going back now.

My gown is raised fully exposing my abdomen and an initial ultrasound examination is performed. I feel very conscious of my body today, it is noticeable that my tummy has changed shape over the preceding few weeks and I cannot help but think I look pregnant whenever I see it. I wish that I was and that all this was just a mistake. Reality check Kate. Comments are made about the bilateral hydronephrosis. Ever inquisitive I turn my head to see the screen and appreciate my own anatomy. An 'X marks the spot' is made for the omental biopsy.

My skin is prepared with what feels like chlorhexidine straight from the freezer which makes me shiver even more. I am asked if I am ok. I tell them to get on with it, but in reality I want to be anywhere but lying on that trolley. A drape is positioned and the local anaesthetic is administered. "This might sting a bit". It doesn't hurt that much and I am numb before I know it. Soon I am being cut. It's a very strange sensation when a scalpel cuts through you own anaesthetised skin. It doesn't hurt, it just feels really weird and I struggle to describe it any further. A warm trickle of blood runs down the outside of my abdomen. Then comes the core biopsy, it is a bit brutal to watch but doesn't really cause me much discomfort. After confirming the position with ultrasound the device is quite literally rammed into the target tissue, a warning given and then a loud click. It is repeated. Two perfect core biopsies are obtained and shown to me for approval. Job done. I almost ask him to do one more just to make sure they have enough tissue. I have sat in so many Haematology MDT meetings as an SHO where the

Histopathologist would have a go at the Radiologist for the inadequacy of specimens. He seems happy enough though and they look like nice chunky pieces of tissue to me so I bite my tongue.

Next it is the nephrostomy. I am given the choice of left or right. I choose left as my right side is already so sore and I usually sleep on my right. This is a bad decision which I am later going to live to regret. Stupidly I ask about local anaesthetic toxicity. I've already had 10mls of 1% lignocaine for the biopsy and I'm worried there will not be enough allowance left to make the nephrostomy procedure bearable. "Don't worry about that my dear, you've got a good covering of subcutaneous fat to absorb it all!"
I respond in a sarcastic manner. "Are you calling me fat? That's charming!" He smiles and beckons me to roll towards him.

The nephrostomy is not a pleasant experience. Again my skin is prepared, drapes positioned and the local administered. Apparently I have low lying twelfth ribs posteriorly which make it that bit more difficult to enter the renal pelvis. It is really sore when the big needle is being poked and prodded around inside me. Comments are again made about my difficult anatomy between him and his Registrar to which I say "that's right, blame the patient!" I really like this Radiologist, it's a good job because I'm going to meet him many more times on this journey. I am repositioned further onto my belly. Eventually he wins the battle he's been fighting and pus coloured urine shoots out under pressure splashing down onto the drapes. I guess all the shivering must have been a rigor. A wire is inserted down the needle then he dilates the tract. I'd been really good at staying quiet and brave through this experience so far but the first dilation is so sore I let out a cry and a tear rolls down my cheek. The kind HCA offers to hold my hand. I accept. Finally after several more dilations, the actual drain is inserted and I'm reassured it's all over. I'm silently sobbing now. The tubing is secured and the site is dressed. 500mls of urine has drained in what seems like no time at all. I'm asked if I want to roll onto my back but I daren't move. I really do not want to go through that experience ever again and am petrified that if I move the nephrostomy would somehow fall out. The Radiologist is rightly concerned about the pus and phones the ward doctors to make sure they put me on antibiotics when I return. I thank him as I'm wheeled out of the torture chamber.

In pain

Life with a nephrostomy is miserable. I arrive back on the ward virtually begging for opiates and am granted a large dose of Oxynorm almost immediately. I overcome my fear of moving by gathering all my mental and physical strength together and with the help of two nurses and a porter transfer from the trolley to my bed with the nephrostomy and my cannula both intact. I cannot believe how much I have changed in my physical abilities in such a short space of time.

The SHO pops in, a lovely girl on the VTS programme who I vaguely know from before. She has been on the phone to the Radiologist about my pyelonephritis. She tells me she is phoning microbiology and that a full set of cultures need to be done. I tell her "don't let them give you any crap, anything less than Tazocin or Meropenem, then I'm not interested!" She smiles and I think she is fairly chuffed with herself when she comes back to tell me Tazocin will be my Domestos. The lovely Consultant from the previous evening also comes by to see me after the procedure ordeal. He is a very gentle personality and breaks all the infection control rules by sitting on the edge of my bed. I'm not sure anyone has actually ever proven sitting on a patient's bed is such a horrendous thing to do and I certainly used to do it all the time. Sometimes being closer to your patient to comfort them when they need you is more important than microbiology. He explains the plan of now waiting for the histology and for my renal function to improve, treating the pyelonephritis and achieving adequate symptom control. He also explains that the medical Gynae-Oncology Consultant team rotate looking after the ward each week so it will be someone new on

Monday. I am disappointed by this news as I trust and like him.

After he leaves I lie in bed staring at the ceiling wishing my renal function to improve and enter the opiated state. This time it goes further, not just the floaty, dizzy feeling but images start to appear on the ceiling tiles. At first pretty 1960s style flowers a la Austin Powers circle around me, but soon the hallucinations become more sinister with hundreds of grim reapers wielding scythes moving towards me. I'm sweating and my heart is pounding. I can rationalise the symptoms are a result of the 10mg dose of Oxynorm and my rubbish creatinine clearance, but it still scares the living daylights out of me.

An uncomfortable weekend is to follow. I limit myself to 2.5mg Oxynorm doses, which does not really provide adequate analgesia, but at least I'm not hallucinating. I never want that to happen again. The on-call Consultant is a Professor in the latter stages of his career. He insists on addressing me as Dr Granger which I find very respectful coming from someone so senior to me but would much rather be called Kate. I describe my pain and nausea and am examined professionally yet gently. "You're in quite a pickle of a situation, aren't you?" He is stating the blooming obvious but he is so nice I don't mind. He listens to my thoughts on symptom control and we agree a management plan. Low dose Oxycontin is commenced and after a quick revision lesson on the pharmacology of anti-emetics we plump for cyclizine. He thinks the sedative effect of regular cyclizine will be a positive given the circumstances. I feel a little bit special when I spy my name is triple underlined on his handover sheet. The hours tick by, but there is no improvement in renal function on the twice daily blood tests despite my prayers. The nephrostomy is draining well and my urine is now clear. The quantity of urine I'm passing per urethra is tailing off and as Monday approaches I know another trip to the torture chamber is on the cards.

Eventually Monday morning arrives. I'm still virtually bed bound and my lack of pain control has become a major issue. When the ward round arrives I am therefore laid in bed feeling very vulnerable. It is led by a new Consultant and there are eight faces staring at me, some of whom I recognise. I am properly freaked out and turn to my nurse, a friendly petite girl with the cutest freckles, to ask if the whole entourage is really necessary. She looks to the Consultant who appears to recognise his mistake in bringing all these people in and the unnecessary doctors dutifully file out. The whole situation reminds me of a lady called Wendy I looked after when I was a Haematology SHO. We used to do 'grand rounds' on Thursdays and sometimes there would be up twelve people standing around a patient's bed, most of who were completely unnecessary and superfluous. Wendy told me one day when I was seeing her alone that she found these huge ward rounds really intimidating especially when she was being examined. As I always used to try and advocate for my patients I made sure that only essential staff saw Wendy from then on and that the Consultant team knew exactly how she felt. She was so touchingly thankful to me. I can now see exactly what she was feeling.

He is a bit 'type A personality' this new Consultant. I am told he cannot take the cancer away and that planning any chemotherapy was going to be difficult in view of my renal problems and recent sepsis, two facts that I had already pondered to a great extent myself and I didn't really need to hear again. I am examined, he is not as gentle as the Professor was and I am really quite sore after he finishes palpating my abdomen, but I stay quiet and try not to wince. I need help to sit forward for the chest examination. I feel really debilitated like one of my elderly patients. I am sweating and comments are made about my temperature although I have remained apyrexial. Then the really bad news, the printout with that day's creatinine is handed to me. He does not issue a warning shot. 429, I cannot help but swear, "oh f**k". My renal function has deteriorated despite the first nephrostomy and this means only one thing, another trip to the torture chamber. He knows that I know this and I am told it has been arranged for later that afternoon. It also means that the left kidney is probably never going to be usefully functional, which makes my general state of health a little bit more precarious.

As he leaves he says we are going to have to work something out about me not wanting to see his Registrar. I know his Registrar fairly well, he is a year or two junior to me and I have taught him on various courses. It isn't as if I have an in-growing toe nail, my problems are so personal that I just wouldn't feel comfortable with him and because of this would probably end up concealing important information from him. I get the feeling that I am causing an inconvenience to the Consultant, but I am well within my rights and say I will have to think about it. He leaves with his scaled down entourage. It feels as though he is trying to guilt trip me in to making his life easier. I'm fuming about the whole debacle but at least it takes my mind off the forthcoming unpleasantness. My Clinical Nurse Specialist has recognised I am not a happy bunny and pops back in after the ward round. I vent my frustrations and she agrees with me. We decide that it would be alright for the Registrar to oversee my care from a distance but if I need examining then someone else would have to see me. A reasonable and rational compromise I think.

The torture chamber revisited

The porter and trolley arrive again. I am wheeled straight into the torture chamber this time and they are all surprised to see me again so soon. They joke about how much I must enjoy spending time in there. I play along although I am really not in the mood. It's a different Consultant, more the 'mad scientist' type but friendly with it. My gown is raised again and I am instructed to roll onto my left side. I am less bothered about my body being exposed today; my dignity seems to be gradually trickling away. It is uncomfortable lying on the existing nephrostomy and I cannot stop thinking to myself how on earth I am going to be able to function when the nephrostomies are bilateral. I lie there and endure the procedure. It's just as bad as the first one and he has exactly the same problems with my anatomy. I accept the offered hand to hold from the off. I don't fight the tears this time either. Soon it's over and the new nephrostomy is draining well, the haematuria is much worse this time but at least there isn't any pus. The bumps on the way back seem like mountains and really hurt even though the porter is trying his very best to give me a smooth ride. When I arrive back, the nurses think the best idea would be to 'Pat-slide' me onto my bed. I'm really not sure about this, but fail an attempt to transfer myself and give in. I'm rolled and the board is slid in under me. "One, two, three, slide". I feel utterly helpless.

Life with two nephrostomies is much more miserable than with just one. I'm struggling to sit myself up in bed due to a terrible stabbing pain at the biopsy site. I have to use the profiling bed to help me. Then once I do manage to sit up I have two drainage bags to contend with that seem to manage to get themselves tangled up at every opportunity.

At least I don't need to use the toilet much anymore, I'm not passing any urine per urethra now and all the opiates have done a grand job at constipating me, so reasons to have to get out of bed are scarce. My pain has continued to be poorly controlled, I just don't seem to be able to get myself comfortable in any position and the smallest of movements is agony. My body has stiffened up with it all which I'm sure is making everything worse. My emotional state is delicate and I think my nurse is struggling to watch my distress. She decides enough is enough and that she is going to get me comfortable before her shift ends in about three hours. She inserts a subcutaneous cannula, a really nifty device I have never seen before that means repeated subcutaneous injections can be given without stabbing the skin each time. She then proceeds to give me alfentanil every half hour until I am relaxed and pain free. It takes five injections. I cannot believe her effort and dedication, but am so thankful that for the first time in what seems like forever I can now actually close my eyes and sleep peacefully.

That night I wake at 3am. It is no surprise that pain has woken me. I'm in so many different pains I don't seem to be able to distinguish them from each other anymore. The staff are so professional on this ward, I barely have to wait two minutes for some Oxynorm. While I am waiting I make a worrying discovery, the 500mls that was in the newly placed right nephrostomy when I went to sleep is still only 500mls. There is air in the tubing. I tell the nurse and she checks the fluid balance chart to make sure it hasn't been emptied in the interim. It hasn't. My luck is not improving. I'm good friends with the SHO on nights who takes her instructions from me and phones the Urologist on call. Between us we try to flush the nephrostomy without success. Yet another trip to torture chamber is scheduled for daylight hours. Sleep is broken and light for the rest of the night.

First thing in the morning I have the pleasure of meeting the Urology team led by an exceptionally dishy Consultant. I am yet to meet a difficult or unhelpful Urologist through my career, considering it's a surgical specialty it really does attract the nicest of the surgical personalities, and some of the best looking! My history is reviewed and they question the American Urologist's decision to do retrograde ureteric stenting first off without covering nephrostomies. He tries to flush the nephrostomy again with no luck. It's sore and he apologises for hurting me. They agree with the need for a nephrostogram and probably reinsertion of the troublesome nephrostomy. A plan to remove my infected stents at flexible cystoscopy is also made for a few days later.

Yet another porter with yet another trolley arrives later that morning. I am wheeled down to the torture chamber for the third time in five days. Both the Radiologists greet me. I'm asked to lie on the fluoroscopy table. It is hard and uncomfortable. The x-rays are shot and the pictures bring devastating news, even I can see the right nephrostomy is sitting in the renal parenchyma no where in the vicinity of the renal pelvis. I ask if it is salvageable but they both shake their heads in unison. It must have moved when I was 'Pat-slided'. The dressings are intact and I had definitely not pulled it myself. As it is removed a horrible internal visceral pain shoots from my back into my anterior abdomen. I don't know if I can go through yet another nephrostomy. I must look frightened, I certainly feel it; the serious Radiologist recognises this, gently rubs my arm and tells me everything is going to be ok. He has quite the human touch for a Radiologist. They have a little conference, comparing their own notes about my anatomy and the mad scientist Radiologist takes on the challenge.

Before I know it I am again laid on my left side with my flank exposed. I close my eyes, hold the HCA's hand and go to my 'happy place' in my mind. This is a deserted beach in Shetland where Chris and I are holding hands and skimming stones into the perfectly blue sea. The air is so fresh and I can almost feel it blowing against my face. I, of course know exactly what is coming as the chlorhexidine is yet again liberally applied to my back. I am in a jumpy state as he scans my back due a combination of pain and anxiety. He is worried he is hurting me, but I tell him to get on with it. Soon it is over and I'm pleased with myself for staying quiet and brave. Perhaps there is something in all this psychological visualisation as a coping strategy after all. He tells me he has gone between the eleventh and twelfth ribs this time so the route inside is much straighter and he has positioned the drain low down in the ureter to reduce the risk of it becoming dislodged again. I'm wheeled out to the recovery area. I pray that this will be my last visit to the torture chamber, at least for a little while.

Trust me to have a rarity

The new right-sided nephrostomy feels much more comfortable than its predecessor from the start and before long it is kicking out buckets of clear urine. The ward staff are having quite a job keeping up with emptying it. I hope for a better creatinine, but the result of 123 is better than I could have wished for. Everything feels just a bit better with normalising renal function, my appetite has returned, the nausea has settled and pain does not seem quite as big an issue.

Although my renal function has rapidly improved my potassium is 6.2 on that afternoon's blood tests. The doctors are a bit slow on the uptake and it's the evening on call FY2 who is given the task to sort it out. I don't really want to roger my veins any further with calcium gluconate and 50% dextrose so my plan would be to do an ECG and repeat the U+Es before taking any drastic action. I can hear the poor FY2 fretting at the nurse's station about what to do. Eventually she summons the courage to see me. I suggest my plan and promise her that given the diuresis that is occurring as we speak that the potassium level will have fallen to below 6 by now. She is unsure and wants to give me calcium anyway. I reassure her to just to do the bloods and send them urgently. The potassium comes back as 5 and I feel vindicated my clinical judgement has not left me yet.

The 'Type A' Consultant comes to see me at lunchtime the following day with a Registrar I've never met. She sits quietly and scribes. They have been at the MDT meeting and he explains that the histology has thrown them a curveball and I had got the Histopathologists scratching their heads. They have characterized it into the 'small round blue cell tumours', which he explains after checking I am ignorant on the subject, are a rare, diverse set of cancers including various sarcomas and lymphomas that usually affect children and teenagers. I am strangely disappointed that despite having a very rare tumour it does not have a cooler name, let's face it not much imagination has gone into 'small round blue cell tumour'! He goes on to explain that the prognosis ranges from the incurable, non-chemosensitive to the completely curable with lasting remission depending on the actual tumour type. He also explains that they need fresh tissue for cytogenetic analysis and further immunohistochemistry, which meant yet another trip to the torture chamber. They are going to fit me later that afternoon at the end of the list.

I'm not quite sure what to make of this news. I thought I had metastatic ovarian cancer, which would have meant a definite death sentence in probably quite a short space of time so at least there is a glimmer of hope that it will be something treatable. However, knowing my recent luck it will probably end up being a bad prognostic type tumour. He tells me my care is being transferred to the Teenage and Young Adult (TYA) team and that the new Consultant will come by to see me the following day. I ask if I will have to move wards. He suggests the Teenage Cancer Unit but I am really not keen on this idea. For a start I like the ward I'm on, I have a side room, the nurses are lovely and I have just about learnt everyone's names. The thought of getting to know a whole new set of people in my current fragile mental state fills me with dread. I also do not really feel like a young adult, I have been married for six years and in my relationship for ten and I do a job with an awful lot of high level responsibility. I probably became middle

43

aged in my early twenties and certainly feel poles apart from a teenager who still needs EMLA cream for a blood test. They listen to my concerns and agree that I can stay where I am.

The serious Radiologist does the second biopsy for me. He doesn't bother with a consent form this time. He seems pleased my renal function is improving. I have always wondered how people working in specialties like Radiology find satisfaction in their jobs. They perform essential procedures and imaging but probably never see many of their patients or the consequences of their work ever again. Much of the satisfaction I achieve from my work is following my patient's journey and seeing how my little contribution to their care hopefully has a positive impact. Apart from not being clever enough it is this for this reason I could never be a Radiologist.

The first biopsy has caused a large haematoma so it is difficult to perform the second one and consequently is much more painful. Unfortunately I was expecting this procedure to be a walk in the park. The HCA says I look pale. He is inspecting the first tissue core by holding it up to the light, when I tell him to do another pass. I have been to the torture chamber every day this week and despite the team being really lovely, I do not want to have to come back tomorrow, no matter how much more immediate pain this means. He obliges although I wish I had stayed quiet as the second pass is worse than the first and I am really sore lying in the recovery area. The HCA is worried about me and keeps repeating my observations. She tells the Radiologist he should do something and he examines the puncture site. I am bleeding a little and firm pressure is applied making my discomfort even worse. I tell them all to stop fussing and get me a porter as soon as possible so I can get back to ward for some drugs. I am becoming quite the little opiate seeker.

Alternative torture chambers

I have been dreading the cystoscopy since the Urologists informed me it was necessary. They told me it will be a quick simple procedure under local anaesthetic but I'm still filled with trepidation and wish I could have some sedation, more to relieve my embarrassment than anything else. I'm wheeled down to the Urology Day Unit to find the team all having a cup of tea and a morning gossip. I am included as I belong to the club. They are a friendly lot. The gossip session goes on for at least twenty minutes until the Registrar decides it's time to get on with some work. "Shall we crack on then?" I nod tentatively. I'm still petrified. We go into the examination room where a bed, scrub table and video screen await me. The Registrar reassures me that it will be over before I know it and that women tolerate the procedure far better than men, maybe something to do with our shorter urethras. He is confident that I will be fine without any sedation. I remove my underwear and get up onto the bed. I am positioned and jump slightly when the nurse cleans me up with warmed antiseptic. I flinch when the Instillagel is applied but I lie back and try to relax. He warns me the scope is about to be inserted and I flinch again as he touches me. It doesn't hurt and before I know it the right stent is out. The left stent is a trickier customer. He is unable to grab it without catching the mucosa and repeats "open, close" instructions to his assistant. It's more uncomfortable now and I've started sweating. He stops, collects himself and adjusts the bed position. This time he has success. I ask to see the stents and two curled discoloured blue plastic stents are shown to me. I'm so glad it's over as I return to the ward. Another tiny bit of dignity has trickled away from me.

The following day I have quite a shock when I'm told that I'm going for my Hickman line. I'd been warned it might be on the cards as it was likely another patient planned for today was going to be cancelled, but this being the NHS I didn't really think it would happen. A nurse hands me a gown and says the theatre staff will be up to collect me in ten minutes. I try to gather my thoughts and get changed. I'm glad it's happening sooner rather than later as it brings the chemotherapy one step closer and my arms are so bruised. It's been less than ten minutes when they come to fetch me. I manage to get myself onto the trolley. A tiny victory for independence, I'm starting to adjust to my new life with bilateral nephrostomies. As I'm pushed down to the basement of the hospital a cheery theatre nurse chats to me all the way. I'm not listening.

As I'm wheeled into the theatre I start with my shivering again. My sympathetic overdrive seems to manifest itself primarily as shivering especially when I am undergoing procedures. I've seen a few Hickman line insertions before so know what to expect and I have consented dozens of patients for the procedure so am well versed on all the risks involved. A tall anaesthetist comes to consent me. The theatre nurse tells him I'm a med reg. His response is "well young lady, have you seen a Hickman line being done before?" I answer "yes". His next question is "have you ever consented anyone for a Hickman line before?" Again I answer "yes, lots of times". He responds "good you'll understand all the risks then. Any questions? Sign here." I'm handed the form and sign my life away. "If you need some drugs for your head then don't be afraid to shout out" he says as he touches my temple with his index finger. I presume by this he means sedation. "Please don't give me a pneumothorax". He chuckles.

47

The trolley is wheeled into the anaesthetic room. I'm hooked up to the monitors and remove my arms from the gown in preparation. We go through to the theatre and I manage to shuffle over to the theatre table. The anaesthetist tells me to protect my nephrostomies and not to worry about my dignity as I try to make sure I don't flash my breasts at all the predominantly male theatre staff. I think to myself it's alright for him, but I still have a tiny little bit of dignity left despite everything. That dignity disappears however when I realise he has draped me with my right breast completely exposed. Lie back and think of England Kate. I continue to shiver. He asks me what practical procedures I like to perform. I think this is his way of distracting me. I say without a doubt a Seldinger chest drain for a pneumothorax. You cannot beat the satisfaction when it's all hooked up and it bubbles away, closely followed by a radial arterial line. He finds and punctures my subclavian vein easily after a quick ultrasound and talks me through what he's doing constantly. I find this extremely reassuring as my head is completely covered with the drapes and I cannot see anything of what is going on. Whilst I lie there I think of all the patients I have inserted central lines into in the past. I was always so scared of the technicalities of the procedure especially not puncturing the carotid artery that often I forgot about my patient and what they were feeling. I promise myself to try and be more like this anaesthetist with his constant reassurances if I ever get back to work. The tunnelling is slightly uncomfortable, but by far the worst bit is when he attaches the skin clip, it feels like he is going to push it through my chest wall. I'm so glad that just for once a procedure is straightforward and tolerable.

Soon I am in recovery and have managed well without any sedation. The site is bleeding and a small trickle of blood runs down over my breast. The scrub nurse puts some pressure on, but the anaesthetist comes out and takes over. I don't like the sight of the blood stained dressings and gown, and I can't wait for it to all be cleaned up. My perfectionism is rearing its ugly head. He talks to me about alternative vascular access should I not get on with the Hickman line and we also talk about how and when the line should be removed. I will be opting for the theatre removal I think as the cuff is high up and I'm not sure I trust a medical SHO or Oncology Registrar's surgical skills enough not to give me a horrible scar, I still have a tiny bit of vanity left even though my dignity has deserted me.

A new boss

The TYA Consultant who I will refer to from now on as DtM for reasons I will not explain here appears later that day as I'm recovering from my Hickman line insertion with his smaller less intimidating team including the female Registrar who had come before with the 'type A' Consultant. He is much more temperate and empathetic in his nature than the 'type A' Consultant and I am impressed as he positions a chair and actually sits down next to my bed instead of standing over me. It must be difficult talking to me, picking the correct level, as although I'm a Physician, I am not an Oncologist and don't know the first thing about 'small round blue cell tumours', so in that respect I must be like any other patient. I do however have a huge chunk of knowledge and experience in the field from my Haematology days. I have been resisting the urge to Google. My background understanding of events is clarified and he checks on my symptom control. He asks to examine me and is unbelievably gentle, so much so I'm not sure he would have actually been able to palpate the pelvic mass. I am glad however he is so gentle as my abdomen remains exquisitely tender. Then he explains everything at just the right level with amazingly adept communication skills. His intuition rightly picks up on my ambivalence towards palliative chemotherapy and he asks is a very subtle way if there were any circumstances where I would refuse treatment. I nod as a tear rolls down my face and instinctively he reaches out to hold my hand. This touch is extremely comforting as inside the distress and turmoil of having to decide between spending months of what life I have left undergoing chemotherapy with all its side effects and simply walking away from the hospital to die properly sets in. We decide to discuss this further once the tumour is characterised and the prognosis is better understood.

It's a Saturday. I wake up in a slightly more positive mood. Until I know what I'm dealing with I'm determined not to waste precious emotional time and energy worrying about it for now. I decide to get myself washed and put on clean pyjamas. I feel a lot better for this and the nurse comments on the nice, fresh smell of my perfume. I hope this is in comparison to her other patients and that I didn't smell awful before. I have to give in and sit down whilst I wash, every time I'm stood up for longer than a few minutes I am overwhelmed by a pre-syncopal feeling, which I'm starting to find quite disabling. I decide to sit out and do my embroidery after my wash, but even the short walk across my side room tires me out and I'm really quite tachypnoeic when the on call Consultant enters. It is another Professor with yet another Registrar in tow. He is pleasant and polite, my history is quickly reviewed and he asks how I am usually as he has obviously never met me before and has clearly noticed the tachypnoea. I admit to the breathlessness fully aware that this will mean a trip to the CT scanner. I'm quizzed for the other symptoms of venous thromboembolism and chest sepsis, none of which I have. He thoroughly examines me, almost as if he was a PACES candidate, but my chest is completely clear. He asks what I think. I say I really hope it isn't a PE but given my history of recent long haul air travel, pelvic malignancy and new onset breathlessness with a normal examination that a CTPA was clinically unavoidable. He agrees and asks the Registrar to arrange this for me.

What seems like a massive dose of Tinzaparin is injected into my abdominal wall and stings so much more than the prophylactic dose. The nurse practitioner draws the short straw cannulating me in preparation for the scan. I cannot understand why my Hickman line cannot be used but I do not argue. She is very professional and obeys the strict local aseptic cannulation policy to the letter. My veins are shot to pieces and I would have struggled to cannulate me, but she finds a non-thrombosed part of an antecubital fossa vein on the right and with a bit of gentle persuasion manages to insert the green venflon demanded by the CT department. I am worrying about my renal function and the intravenous contrast.

I feel honoured to be having a CTPA on a weekend, no less than VIP treatment for me. Another trolley arrives and another ride around the corridors and lifts of the newly built cancer hospital. It's much quieter at the weekend without the usual hustle and bustle and I notice that despite it being nearly brand new the hospital is starting to look a bit shabby around the edges. We reach the CT scanner and I realise I haven't had a CT since I was in America and would rather forget that experience. At least today's scan will not involve any rectal contrast. Whilst I'm waiting it pops into my mind that when they give you the intravenous contrast for a CTPA it is supposed to feel like you are being incontinent of urine. I wonder if this will happen in my current urological predicament. All my tubes and lines are transferred over to the scanner table which is quite a rigmarole that I am becoming well rehearsed at. My precious green venflon is hooked up to the contrast machine and the scan begins. I'm asked to take a deep breath and am moved quickly through the scanner. That's it; it takes literally less than a minute. I wonder why Radiologists are so reluctant to do CTPAs out of hours. There is no feeling of incontinence or flushing.

I find out later in the day that luckily the scan is negative for pulmonary embolism and only shows some mild basal atelectasis and tiny bilateral pleural effusions, which is hardly surprising as my albumin has plummeted to 20. On the positive side the scan does not show any evidence of pulmonary metastases. We attribute the breathlessness to all the procedures, anaemia and physical deconditioning. In view of this I try to build up my exercise tolerance a little by taking a stroll around the ward but am soon back in bed due to the dizziness, I will try again tomorrow.

It is a bank holiday Monday, the hospital remains quiet and I have some time to myself to think. I cannot really comprehend everything I have been through in the past few weeks. It doesn't feel as if it has happened to me although I have the scars, tubes and pain to prove it. I feel as though I am looking in on my life from the outside. When you are in your twenties you really think you are invincible. Life was going so great, my career was going really well, I had a lovely husband, brilliant friends and no money worries. How has all this happened to me? Occasionally I wake up when I have managed to sleep and for a split second I will have forgotten all about the illness then I will remember the nightmare and am overwhelmed by a terrible sinking internal feeling. DtM is on call and pops by to see me. I am fed up with the whole situation today and tell him so. He tells me that getting gloomy about it all won't help anyone especially myself and I suppose he is right. My positive mood has not lasted that long but I don't think anybody would begrudge me feeling blue once in a while given the circumstances. He explains they are teeing me up for chemotherapy in the next couple of days, it will be a best guess of agents and a scaled down dose given my recent renal failure and sepsis, but my health is not improving and that is mainly due to the cancer.

Yet another hurdle for me to tackle. In preparation for this he pulls a crumpled consent form out of his pocket. He talks as he scrawls on it. It is proper unreadable doctor scrawl too. Mum always says my hand writing is way too neat to belong to a doctor. Sickness, hair loss and the consequences of myelosuppression seem to be the main messages. I of course know from experience that doxorubicin can cause heart problems and cyclophosphamide can cause haemorrhagic cystitis and increases the risk of secondary cancers. I don't suppose I will survive long enough to worry about the latter too much though. He doesn't mention these other risks but I'm sure he knows that I already know. I spend the rest of the day wondering which of the side effects I will experience.

The next day my creatinine has flicked up to 195 and the right nephrostomy output has tailed off a little. The ratio of right to left volumes produced had been running steadily at two to one but it is more like one to one now. I am therefore worried about the patency of right nephrostomy and basically tell the SHO that this development needs discussing with a Radiologist, preferably one of the two that know me well, without giving him the opportunity to argue with me. We are not going to be messing around with my renal function no matter how small the deterioration. I need to get well enough for chemotherapy and fast. He returns after discussing my case with a Radiology Registrar who has suggested an ultrasound followed by a nephrostogram depending on the ultrasound results. I cannot see the clinical point of an ultrasound but as it is a non-invasive test I do not dispute it.

The porter arrives soon after and I am wheeled down to Radiology but instead of being delivered to the ultrasound department as expected I am parked up outside the torture chamber. I wait for about half an hour. It must be liver biopsy afternoon as there are three very jaundiced looking patients lined up on the trolleys. In time the serious Radiologist appears and goes over my recent history and concerns. He tells me an ultrasound is a pointless investigation in this situation and that a nephrostogram is the most appropriate test. It will also probably be therapeutic if there is a kink. He has intercepted the request card in the department and I feel a bit special to have my own personal Radiologist looking out for me. We go through to the fluoroscopy room and I am asked to lie on the table. He says I must be getting used to all these procedures by now, I say I am but it doesn't make it any easier though. I am certainly more nimble moving around with all my baggage now and do not need any help to position myself. For what seems like the fiftieth time I sign the form to say I am not pregnant. They shoot pictures without contrast first and I am relieved to see both nephrostomies sitting low down in my ureters. I am becoming quite adept at the interpretation of fluoroscopy images now. The contrast is injected next, he warns me it might hurt a little but towards the end of the injection a horrible searing pain shoots from my right loin to right iliac fossa. I am unprepared for such a severe pain and take a sharp intake of breath trying to be brave and not to let it show. The pictures are shot again and look reasonable with good contrast flow. He helps me to sit up and reassures me that everything looks fine. I am still in pain and he apologises for hurting me as I limp back to my wheelchair. My creatinine that evening falls to 130 so perhaps the nephrostogram was therapeutic after all.

I am given the baby dose of chemotherapy the following day. It consists of just two infusions, one of doxorubicin and one of cyclophosphamide followed by a bag of Mesna. I have them all scratching their heads as to whether I would be able to get haemorrhagic cystitis when my bladder is not in use. They of course give the Mesna anyway, not wanting to take any risks. The vomiting kicks in about twelve hours after the infusions are completed. It almost takes me by surprise. I don't know why, I knew to expect it. The nurses pump me full of ondansetron and dexamethasone. I am really struggling to swallow the tablets as every time I try it just sets off more retching then vomiting. My Oxycontin ends up in a vomit bowl several times and I worry about my pain returning although it seems under reasonable control despite missing doses. I can feel the steroids messing with my head. It is really weird but I feel very edgy and snappy, which is not like me as I have been very calm and placid through all this and haven't been through an angry stage. Chris has though and has ongoing problems with this. I vow that next time I am not going to take them and make a mental note to discuss this with the Consultant the next time I see him. The following two days are miserable, but it eventually abates and I start to feel better and can nibble on proper food again.

The SHO has become obsessed by my magnesium level which seems to plummet whenever I don't eat. I have no idea why the Oncologists are so fixated with magnesium levels. As far as I'm concerned they only really clinically

56

matter with arrhythmias, seizures and refeeding syndrome none of which I have or am likely to develop. He has prescribed magnesium oxide tablets for me which are the most massive, horrible capsules that I would have struggled to swallow even before I was ill and in my current delicate state would not have a hope in hell of getting down. I argue this point with him, show him the tablets and ask if he would take them if he was feeling nauseated. He suggests opening the capsules up and dissolving the contents, an idea that seems even worse to me because then I would be able to taste its vile contents. As he does not seem able to appreciate my point of view I decide to be a difficult patient and put my foot down. I issue an ultimatum, either he stops worrying about and indeed measuring my magnesium level or he replaces it in my intravenous fluids. I will not be under any circumstances taking the tablets. He opts to put some magnesium sulphate in my fluids. I have been trying my hardest to be friendly, pleasant and not scary to the junior doctors looking after me, but I fail today. Never mind.

The episode reminds me of my Cardiology boss when I was an SHO. She was a proper old school wise Consultant but was also quite progressive in her training methods. At the beginning of a rotation she would make all her junior staff and medical students take commonly prescribed unpalatable remedies such as potassium supplements and laxatives. This had had a huge impact on me and meant I would always think twice before I scribbled something on a drug chart flippantly. Perhaps this SHO would have also benefited from her lesson.

Worst case scenario

I have not quite worked out DtM's schedule yet as he seems to appear at random times so I am not prepared mentally when the ward round arrives this morning. He brings his Registrar and two SHOs. The Registrar sits in the corner and the two SHOs stand awkwardly at the end of my bed. The female one does the scribing and the male one tries his hardest not to make eye contact with me after yesterday's dressing down. DtM asks how I've been and it is nice to report the nausea is settling and I'm gradually increasing my fluid intake instead of complaining about something or other. He seems genuinely pleased.

He then addresses the issue of definitive diagnosis, which has finally been made after lots of immunohistochemistry and cytogenetics. It is a desmoplastic small round cell tumour (DSRCT). This news hits me hard and I am not ready to hear it. I had given in to my urge to research what was going on the previous evening and had done some preliminary reading on the iPad about the infamous 'small round blue cell tumours'. I was hoping it might be a lymphoma or a rhabdomyosarcoma. All that I had read about DSRCT was that it was an extremely aggressive tumour with poor response to chemotherapy and dismal survival rates, and in the whole grand scheme of 'small round blue cell tumours' was not a good one to have. I stay quiet and stare at the end of my bed letting the diagnosis settle in. Everyone remains silent. Soon I am crying. He asks if I have been reading, which I admit to and he gently asks what I understand so far. I manage to say that I know it is really bad prognostically but I'm properly crying now and cannot really speak intelligently anymore. I signal for the SHOs to leave the room, its bad enough breaking down emotionally without juniors staring at me whilst I do. I apologise to DtM for disbanding his team but he doesn't seem to mind. He has a plan which involves me going home once my renal function is stable off intravenous fluids and to come back next week to see him in clinic to hopefully be admitted for proper chemotherapy that day. The thought of discharge lifts the metaphorical dark black cloud hanging over me a little.

He asks if I want to go ahead with more chemotherapy given the fact that this is very much a palliative situation now with no hope of cure. I have felt comfortable from the outset with him to make my own opinion of Oncology clear so he knows that I think they flog their patients, especially the younger ones with horrendous treatments until the last possible moment despite incurability. I am a conservative Physician and believe passionately that quality of life is much more important than quantity of life in the palliative care setting and why would I not apply these principles to my own care. I do not want to be hooked up to chemotherapy hoping for some non-existent miracle when I am on my death bed. I do however feel obliged to give proper chemotherapy a try, more for Chris and the family than for myself and do not really feel I have a choice at this stage.
"You absolutely do have a choice, you can go home and be looked after and no-one here will question that decision if that is what you choose to do."
We then discuss that I probably have more to lose not giving treatment a try than going ahead with it especially in terms of symptom control as in his experience chemotherapy is usually effective in reducing pain in this condition even if it does not cause tumour shrinkage. I have been gently manipulated into accepting treatment

59

almost without me knowing it, but I don't mind, it seems the right way forward for now.

Escape

I start to prepare for my escape. I have always enjoyed a good meaty bit of discharge planning and when done well it can make such a big difference. I have been in hospital for over three weeks and there are a lot of things to consider as I will be leaving hospital a very different person from the one that was admitted. The Oncology doctors do not seem all that interested in planning my discharge and the TTO that has been prepared in advance is sadly lacking in information and the drugs are inaccurate. So I decide to take back a little control and do the planning myself. I make a list. There are lots of medical supplies I will need at home to look after my line and nephrostomies. I want some Nozinan injections as a rescue treatment in case I run into problems with nausea and vomiting in addition to the other medications I am taking. I also need a new sick note, all the emergency contact numbers and to have a practice on the stairs. District nurse visits and blood tests will also require arranging for whilst I'm away from the hospital. The ward sister does the collecting together of equipment and returns with three huge bags of stuff.

I try the stairs when Mum, Dad and Chris are visiting. Typically I go at the task like a bull in the china shop and walk down all the stairs from the fifth floor to the shop to buy a drink. On the way back I decide to tackle a couple of flights going up the way. I am disappointed when I only manage one flight, limited by breathlessness. As we all stand in the lift I start to feel extremely pre-syncopal. I have buzzing in my ears, my vision is blurring and I am sweating. I lean against the lift wall and contract my calf muscles to improve my venous return. Dad looks worried, I must be looking pale. He takes my arm. Soon I am back on the ward and after a short lie down and a piece of chocolate I am back to my usual self. It is a wake up call though that I am going to have to take things at a slower pace than I'm used to when I do finally get home. I keep the near syncopal event to myself as I'm not going to let a little fainting do stop me from escaping.

I manage to make my escape the following day. It takes Chris three trips to shift all the stuff I have accumulated over the past month. My room had become quite a little home from home with photographs, a radio, television, iPod speakers, books and the like. I try to help but the dizziness is still there and I'm not much use. I do manage to take down all the cards we have blu-tacked to the notice board and even that I have to do in stages. There are well over fifty. I didn't realise so many people cared about me before all this. I have written a heart felt card to the ward staff thanking them all for their brilliant care, praising the well run ward as a whole and we hand over the statutory chocolates and biscuits. We leave with all the necessary supplies and everything arranged perfectly. It won't be long until I am back again.

An Ally

There is someone who I haven't mentioned yet who really helped me through the past few weeks, the Palliative Medicine Registrar. I first met him the day after I moved to the cancer hospital as his expertise had been called upon to help with analgesia, which given my appalling renal function at the time was challenging. He is a shy but endearing character and I instantly like and trust him. I soon discover we share very similar views and principles about medicine in general and palliative care in particular. He is not at all patronising but is obviously more knowledgeable than me about analgesia in the context of renal failure. I have used alfentanil a couple of times in the past in conjunction with the palliative care team but would never be confident enough to prescribe it independently. His suggestions really help with getting me more comfortable. He visits most days, I am not sure this is really necessary but I find it comforting. He has much more time to sit and chat than the Oncologists which helps me come to terms with my impending mortality. We explore my expectations around death when the time comes. He is very easy to talk to and I do not become distressed during these difficult conversations.

It is a touch awkward one day when he pops by whilst my parents are visiting. I had not told them I was seeing a Palliative Care doctor, but he is very professional and explains he is helping with my symptom control instead of announcing his full title. We soon develop an 'us and them' type rapport with the 'them' being the Oncologists especially when I am under the 'type A' Consultant. He shields me from the palliative care nurses in the hospital and also doesn't think that a community Macmillan nurse referral is appropriate at this stage especially as my GP seems on the ball. I am pleased about this as I have met so many people over recent weeks and more new faces can sometimes be more counter-productive than useful. I also think we would struggle to find a Macmillan nurse I would be able to develop a good rapport with and he agrees with me on this. The nurses on the ward fulfil much of the Macmillan role anyway, there are a couple in particular who I really get on with and they seem to have time for a chat when I need to talk.

He is extremely supportive when I receive the news about definitive diagnosis and spends well over an hour with me that day. It really helps to talk about my fears, expectations and doubts about the treatment and I am much more able to rationalise my feelings after our chat. Unlike with the Oncologists I am not embarrassed about crying during this consultation. He seems a bit upset that it is not better news, but I guess we both knew it wasn't going to be.

A home visit

I've been at home for two days now. It is so lovely to be around my own things and my sofa is a damn site more comfortable than a hospital bed. One thing is plaguing my return home though. I'm so constipated. It hadn't really bothered me in hospital as I wasn't really eating but my now my appetite had picked up the constipation has become properly symptomatic. I've never had this problem before in my life, but I can now really empathise with my older patients who land up in hospital with it. It seems a bit lame to be asking the GP to do a home visit for constipation but there is no way I can go to the surgery in my current state and I've got to get it sorted out. The receptionist is lovely on the phone and promises me a visit by lunchtime. The GP arrives and perches on our small sofa. I tell him the devastating news about the diagnosis and as I know he will have never heard of the condition before I have printed out two of the best review articles I have read on the subject. He seems grateful I have made this effort for him. I'm a bit embarrassed about my bowel issues but get on with describing my symptoms. He listens and nods a lot. I feel a bit stupid when asked to clarify exactly what I mean by constipation. We negotiate a treatment plan including Microlax enemas and laxatives. After an update about what has happened in hospital and a request for a community DNAR order he leaves.

Two days later I am no better and Chris requests another visit. I am still embarrassed about all this, but the GP remains professional. It is really nice to be able to see the same doctor each time. My abdominal pain is worse due to all the straining so I position myself on the sofa for an abdominal examination. The left iliac fossa is really quite tender on palpation, a new pain for me. He reassures me that my bowel sounds are not obstructed. He asks me what I think is going on and seems to want to exploit my expertise. The differential lies between constipation and tumour pain, but I am really reluctant to increase my opiate dose as this will worsen the constipation. He agrees that this seems logical and suggests that asking the district nurses to give me a proper enema might be the best way forward. He almost apologises for the fact that he will need to perform a rectal examination and starts explaining the clinical rationale for this. I interrupt, say I understand and give my consent. I am glad he wants to do a PR and was hoping he might; the very act of the examination will probably help move things on a little so to speak. My dignity must be almost at zero now as I would never have thought like this before I was ill.

We go upstairs to the bedroom. I'm breathless walking upstairs and a bit dizzy when I reach the top. I get myself ready and he finds himself instructing me to lie on my left side with my knees up, more out of habit than remembering I was an experienced doctor who had performed numerous PR exams and knew exactly how I needed to position myself. I used to have a reputation at work for being the 'PR queen', there is usually a good clinical reason to perform one in most elderly patients if you think about it enough and I was always brought up to consider it part of a thorough examination so never shied away from it. He apologises again and gets on with the examination. I wasn't expecting it to be sore, but on palpation anteriorly he really hurts me and my body stiffens. He senses this and asks if he's hurting me, I answer in the affirmative and he stops. It turns out the tumour is causing a large amount of extrinsic compression on my rectum. I ponder this for the rest of the day. A distal bowel obstruction was not in my plan for a serene, dignified death at home, but the thought of a colostomy appals me. I really could not cope with that on top of the bilateral nephrostomies. I decide to stop dwelling on it and keep pouring the laxatives in from the top end. Soon I have some success.

A trip to clinic

Chris comes with me to this first sarcoma clinic appointment. DtM had made me promise to bring him as he wants to talk to him. I think he thinks that I am not sharing everything with Chris although I did try to protect and shield him initially I have been completely honest and open with him since we returned to the UK. I feel a little bit more normal today as I have adorned my leg bags and put my favourite maxi dress on. It is nice to be wearing something girly instead of pyjamas. We sit in the waiting room and people watch, a beloved pastime of ours. I am the youngest patient in the waiting room by a long way. We observe that most of the patients when asked how they are by the doctors and nurses, respond "fine, thank you". We chuckle to each other about how ironic this is given the fact we are sat in an Oncology clinic although I suppose some of them must be in remission. An old man sits behind us waiting for his appointment in the lung cancer clinic. He has a really fruity, productive cough. Chris is not impressed. I'm sure he would wrap me up in cotton wool if he could. We had arrived early and the clinic was already running late so it seems as though we have been sat for a long time when DtM finally comes to get us. I am pleased he has spotted us in the waiting room and doesn't just shout out my name, another gentle touch that impresses me. I introduce Chris and he shakes his hand.

We go through to his consultation room. The chairs are arranged in a semicircle around his desk. It is an extremely windy day and it whistles through the building making the structure shudder. He makes a start by asking how I've been. I respond "surprisingly alright". We talk about the problems I've had with constipation and dizziness, but despite these symptoms I give a positive vibe and say I am generally better in myself from when I last saw him. He seems pleased I have improved. My only new complaint is night-time back pain and we check my MRI report to see if the bone metastases correlate with the site of the pain, which they do. He half heartedly offers radiotherapy but this will delay chemotherapy and I am not finding this pain hugely intrusive. We decide to monitor my symptoms for the moment. He requests to "put a hand on my tummy" and we go through to the examination room. I realise my choice of clothes was not particularly practical as I lie on the couch but he doesn't seem to mind and palpates my abdomen through my dress. It's much more comfortable than before and I hardly wince at all. The pelvic mass remains prominent and easily palpable, but he thinks it is about the same size as before.

He asks if I have had any more thoughts about chemotherapy and I say I have made a decision to go through with it, at least for the moment to see how bearable the treatment is. He tells me about the limited evidence base for treatment protocols, but I have been doing some reading at home and am now well researched and knowledgeable on my condition. As I expected he suggests the Kushner protocol which involves seven cycles of high dose inpatient chemotherapy using various combinations of doxorubicin, cyclophosphamide, vincristine, etoposide and ifosfamide. There is a high risk of neutropaenic sepsis especially given the presence of my nephrostomies.

After all the high level medical chat that has been going on, he turns to Chris and asks what he understands about my illness so far. I am proud of him for keeping his composure and giving a sensible, realistic answer that shows he understands the palliative nature of my condition. He seems satisfied and I turn to DtM and say "see, I haven't been telling any fibs!" He smiles and leans back on his chair.

We meet the sarcoma Clinical Nurse Specialist after my appointment with DtM. She is lovely but seems a little overawed by my profession. We talk about the treatment plan and a little about how I initially presented. She gives me her contact details and promises to visit during the first proper cycle of chemotherapy.

Round one

I am admitted to my usual ward later that day to start my treatment after Chris and I share chilli con carne in the hospital canteen. My nurse is one my favourites and shares my name. Having in-patient chemotherapy is a labour intensive business from a nursing perspective. After two nurses double check my identity, wristbands and prescriptions my line is accessed, I am pre-medicated with ondansetron and dexamethasone and she starts the vincristine. This takes about ten minutes to infuse and the infusion needs to be supervised throughout so she redresses my nephrostomies and Hickman line whilst we wait. All the best nurses are brilliant at multi-tasking. It is a nice sensation having my dressings removed and the sites cleaned with cooling chlorhexidine. They get so itchy at times. Next the doxorubicin, which as its name would suggest is a red liquid. I watch as it creeps down the giving set replacing the saline in the line. Soon it is past the pump and coming up the tubing towards me. I don't feel any different as it enters my bloodstream but I know the vomiting will set in soon enough after last time. Once the doxorubicin is through I press my buzzer and the cyclophosphamide mesna combination is commenced which is a six hour infusion. The infusion is covered with a dark brown plastic bag to protect it from the light. For some reason it makes me think of an executioner wearing a hood.

I manage to sleep reasonably well only to be awoken at 6am by an overwhelming wave of nausea. I sit bolt upright in bed, reach for an emesis basin and vomit violently. I continue like this for half an hour until I run out of sick bowls and press my buzzer for more. A male healthcare assistant obliges and dutifully removes my vomit. My abdominal muscles ache from all the retching and I feel truly awful. I hate vomiting. I could never be bulimic. The regimen involves two more doses of doxorubicin and cyclophosphamide and I wonder how I am going to survive it. They try more intravenous ondansetron without success.

DtM pokes his head around the curtain to find me sick bowl in hand. I reprimand him for making feel so horrendous with his poisons and he plays along, pretending to leave. I manage a smile. However, I really am at the end of my tether now and unusually for me relinquish control over choice of anti-emetics. "Just make it stop". I feel totally pathetic. A syringe driver with cyclizine and haloperidol is prescribed with some, but not total relief of the nausea. I manage to sip on some water, but am constantly worrying about my nephrostomy output, as my oral intake has been negligible and my urine is becoming gradually more concentrated. I persuade an SHO some supplementary intravenous fluids might be a good idea whilst I'm like this.

The Palliative Care Registrar comes to visit soon after the Consultant and thinks that levomepromazine would be a better choice for the syringe driver given the severity of my symptoms. I am pleased he has chosen this as I have had lots of positive experience using it in the past and it always seems to be effective when everything else fails. I can also see that the side effect of drowsiness might be quite nice as I am exhausted. He doesn't stay long as I have my head in a vomit bowl. I apologise as he leaves and he tells me not to be silly. The nurses are so good and my syringe driver is changed over immediately.

That afternoon one of the scariest things to happen to me so far occurs. I am laid in bed starting to feel drowsy from the Nozinan. Chris is here but I am not up to chatting really. Suddenly I have the urge to open my bowels and we have a struggle to get me out of bed in time with the massive tangle of wires and tubes. With Chris's help I manage to reach the toilet and have an episode of diarrhoea quite out the blue. It is not offensive and I am not particularly worried about infection. As I get comfortable in bed again a horrendous central sharp abdominal pain overwhelms me. It is proper ten out ten pain and so sudden in onset. I am sweating and shivering and don't know whether to move about or lie completely still. I plump for the latter. Chris is really worried and struggles to watch my distress, he wants to call someone straight away but I just want to see if it passes before I bother anyone. It doesn't pass and we press the buzzer. As I am not a buzzer happy patient the nurses usually respond very quickly when I do press. The sister appears and looks worried. I must have looked awful and have now started retching. My pulse is 140, respiratory rate is 36 and I have a low-grade pyrexia. She immediately contacts a doctor and fetches some subcutaneous Oxynorm. I am relieved she treats my pain so quickly and efficiently as I do not think I could have experienced that level of agony for much longer.

As I start to settle she takes bloods from my line and puts up a fluid challenge even before the doctor arrives. I now start to worry about the long differential of acute abdominal pain in patients on chemotherapy including cyclophosphamide induced pancreatitis and bowel perforation. It is the magnesium SHO who has drawn the short straw. He examines me and I am extremely tender centrally, but there is no guarding or rebound tenderness to my great relief. The pain soon returns as the Oxynorm wears off, but the sister is on the ball and soon has me comfy again. The Registrar comes up from clinic to see me and thinks we should get an erect chest and abdominal X-ray done to rule out perforation, wait on the bloods and continue with analgesia as prescribed.

I need another three Oxynorm injections whilst we wait for the porters to take me to Radiology. It is late when the porters do eventually arrive and I am glad they have brought a trolley for me. They take me to the old part of the hospital next to the Emergency Department. One of the Emergency Medicine Consultants I used to work for wanders down the corridor in the opposite direction. He recognises me immediately and there then follows an awkward conversation about my illness. I don't know why but I am embarrassed and a bit ashamed about everything. My trolley is parked up in the Radiology waiting area. The department is heaving with people most of who appear to have injuries consistent with fighting. The porter tells the radiographer I am a doctor and she queue jumps me straight into the X-ray room. There aren't many perks from being in this business. The X-rays look good and I suggest a trying PPI which miraculously cures the pain. I cannot believe gastritis could cause so much misery but clearly it can.

The last doses of the chemotherapy have to be delayed due to the acute abdominal pain episode so are given the following day. It is much easier with the Nozinan syringe driver. It makes my vision blurry and me drowsy but I really don't mind if it means I am not vomiting. I make my escape the following day to await the neutropaenic sepsis.

Zero neutrophils

I have been out of hospital for a few days when the rigoring starts. Chris and I had just returned from a night away at Center Parcs with some friends and had only been back in the house for half an hour. I know exactly what is happening and have been expecting it. My mouth has been so sore I could barely eat so I'm sure I must be neutropaenic by now. Having a rigor with oral mucositis is not pleasant, the uncontrollable teeth chattering is really starting to hurt my tongue and buccal mucosa. I climb into bed and try to get warm. Chris finds me and panics. I often forget that he has no experience of all this and it must be scary for him. I have seen hundreds of patients having rigors in my time so I manage to stay calm and reassure Chris that it's nothing to worry about, we just need to phone the hospital. He dutifully does so and they send an ambulance for me as it is fast approaching rush hour.

The crew arrive, I tell them I'm a doctor, give them a rapid clinical summary and ask to be taken to ward 95 at St James's. They are a little flustered by my profession but luckily the paramedic on the crew used to be a healthcare assistant on an Oncology ward so knows all about neutropaenic sepsis. Their dispatch team had told them I was going to Pinderfields but I am firm about the need to go to Jimmy's. I do not want to go anywhere near Pinderfields at any cost. Luckily they listen to me. I am helped into the ambulance and lie on their trolley. My temperature is up to 37.8°C now and my pulse is 140. They decide blues and twos down the motorway would be appropriate. I am starting to feel very unwell now and accept the offered oxygen as my saturations are only 94% on air. By the time we arrive at St James's I have started to feel a little better and almost feel a fraud as I am wheeled onto the assessment unit.

Day 1   Hb 9.5 WCC 0.15 Neuts 0.03 Platelets 73
My Registrar is on call and is on the assessment unit as I arrive. She seems a bit miffed that no-one has told her about my imminent arrival. I get the feeling she is a very in control sort of Registrar and likes to know exactly what is going on, a bit like myself. I'm sure the juniors are all a little bit scared of her, but that she is well respected amongst them. It is nice that she knows me so I do not have to go through everything and I give her a rapid account of what has happened. She examines me concisely and I am receiving Tazocin before I know it. The Sister is familiar, she recognises me too and we work out that we must have worked together on the Medical Admissions Unit at Leeds General Infirmary. There follows some reminiscing about the 'good old days' and some of the characters we used to look after and work with. She finds me a side room to be admitted into and I am grateful for this. When my blood results come back I am impressed by the degree of my neutropaenia.

Day 2   Hb 8.0 WCC 0.08 Neuts 0.06 Platelets 38
The 'type A' Consultant is on call today and pops by to check on me with a pasty looking male Registrar. I have woken up with a severe occipital headache today but he doesn't seem to think this is anything to worry about although he doesn't examine me. I am reassured that the antibiotics and fluids will do the job and I will just have to sit out the myelosuppression. I am not warming to him any. He literally stays for about two minutes. I move back to my usual ward later that day and feel more comfortable with familiar faces around me. I start with heavy PV

bleeding in the evening. It's probably just because I am thrombocytopaenic but I tell the doctors anyway. They want to give me tranexamic acid but I really do not want to take this with the venous thromboembolism risk and the nephrostomies. I confirm this is the right decision with my haematology friends on email and they agree. I have some good colleagues to back up my decision making.

Day 3   Hb 7.5 WCC 0.08 Neuts 0.02 Platelets 16
The daily routine of intravenous antibiotics, changing fluids and emptying nephrostomies continues. I am totally washed out today and cannot get out of bed without help due to severe dizziness when I stand. I am therefore not surprised my haemoglobin is only 7.5. The Consultants are away at a sarcoma conference so the Registrar is running the show, she already has her CCT and a Consultant post lined up so is all but a boss anyway. Coping with the bone marrow failure is much worse than I had anticipated. I catch a glimpse of myself in the mirror and cannot believe how grey and ill I look.

I need to be transfused today with both packed cells and platelets. I am given three units of the red stuff without any problems and it is amazing how my lips have turned from grey to pink in such a short space of time. Unfortunately the dizziness persists but as I recently learned transfused cells are not capable of oxygen carriage until at least twenty four hours after transfusion so I guess I will have to wait for the symptomatic improvement. I am petrified about the platelet transfusion, probably needlessly so but again this is one of those times where I wished I could erase some of my experience. The last patient I gave platelets to died as the donation had been contaminated with Klebsiella. It was a very sudden

77

deterioration and there was nothing anybody could do, but the whole episode had really traumatised me and knocked my confidence as a doctor. The thought of having platelets transfused into me was therefore hugely scary although I know full well that episode was a one in a million event and there was no real reason to worry about the transfusion at all. The bag is attached to my line and as the yellow fluid creeps up the line towards me I tell myself not to be stupid. There is no reaction and it is just like any other infusion I have had.

Day 4   Hb 10.0 WCC 0.19 Neuts 0.04 Platelets 50
I wake up in the early hours of the morning today to discover a wet sheet beneath me. As I come round and am still a little dazed I have a horrible sinking feeling that I have wet the bed but then I realise that would not be anatomically possible as I reach full consciousness. I inspect my nephrostomy sites and the right sided dressings are soaked through. The nurses are lovely about it, change my bed and dressings immediately and contact the on call doctor for me. It is bad enough coping with nephrostomies, never mind coping with leaking nephrostomies. They will have to find a solution even if that means a trip to the torture chamber; I cannot go home like this. Whilst I await the night doctor they give me a plastic absorbent blue sheet to lie on, it is just like what they would do for an incontinent eighty year old patient. I am embarrassed. There is nothing the on call doctor can really do but she promises to make sure it is handed over so my team can sort it out in the morning.

I am wheeled down to Radiology later that day. The porter parks me in an empty waiting room which I am pleased about given my virtually non-existent immune system.

Unfortunately I am soon joined by an older man on a trolley who is pushed in by another porter wearing a yellow apron. This is a symbol in this hospital that a patient is infected with something nasty like C. difficile or MRSA. The poor man is verging on having a death rattle and probably was not well enough to be left alone in a Radiology department. The porter leaves his trolley right next to me. Although I am sympathetic that he is clearly not very well I turn and try to breathe in the other direction. Soon we are also joined by another patient and her family. The granddaughter has the worst smoker's cough I have ever heard and doesn't cover her mouth. So I am surrounded by germs with no neutrophils for over half an hour. It is a blessed relief when they finally fetch me into the torture chamber.

It is a Radiology Fellow who performs the procedure but he has had a good chat with the serious Radiologist about me and has his instructions so I am reassured. He seems very experienced and has a dry sense of humour. The nephrostogram is painful like before but I try not to let it show. It is difficult to identify the leaking point but he thinks the best option would just be to replace the whole system. I agree. He warns me that he will have to dilate the renal tract with more contrast than the initial nephrostogram and if I had felt that then it will be quite a lot more painful. I thought I had done a good job covering up my discomfort initially but clearly not. I tell him the pain is nothing is comparison to actually having the nephrostomy done in the first place so just to crack on. I am rolled onto my left side and a blanket is wedged under me. First a wire is inserted down the existing nephrostomy, then the tube is removed over the wire and this is accompanied by pain and the sensation of warm fluid flowing down my back. I ask if this is blood, but am reassured it is only a mixture of contrast and urine. I apologise for being an anxious patient. The new nephrostomy is positioned and after a quick X-ray to confirm position it is pretty much over. Clean fresh dressings are applied and I am allowed to sit up. He scrolls through the images on the screen for me so I can see exactly what he has done. I am disappointed to see no contrast whatsoever trickling through my distal ureter but I suppose it is early days.

Losing my marbles and my hair
Day 5   Hb 10.3 WCC 0.16 Neuts 0.02 Platelets 66

I am getting despondent now about the myelosuppression. I did not realise that I would be so profoundly neutropaenic for such a long period. My mouth is sore and I am barely eating because of it. The dizziness is better and my temperature has settled though. The new nephrostomy is behaving itself and appears to drain better than the old one. The nurses comment I am not my usual bubbly chatty self and ask about my mental health. This makes me well up. I know I am not coping well this week mentally and am starting to have serious doubts about whether I want to continue down this path. Another six cycles does not seem survivable to me if I have to encounter all these problems every time. The quality of life that is so important to me just isn't there. I do not voice all my inner thoughts to the nurses but wish I could talk to DtM. He isn't back from his conference for another three days.

Day 6   Hb 9.2 WCC 0.2 Neuts 0.06 Platelets 66

My hair started falling out about a week ago. Initially it was just a few hairs here and there but now it was coming out in huge clumps. I cannot help but pull it out and roll the hair into balls. I find myself doing it even without realising. My scalp is so itchy. I decide enough is enough and it needs to go. I think I would rather it happened in hospital so the mess is easier to tidy up. I have very thick hair. One of the first things I did when we got back from America after visiting the GP of course was to go and see the hairdresser. She was a lovely girl who understood as her mum had just been having treatment for breast cancer and had lost her hair. She recommended me having my hair cut into a bob style so I would get out of the habit of being able to tie it back and then if I did lose it, it would be easier to manage. She had been absolutely right and everyone had loved my new style while it lasted. The healthcare assistants borrow some clippers off the teenage unit and get to work for me. I am surprisingly emotionless about the experience and they comment how brave I am being. I have always loved my hair so much but I know it needs to happen and there is absolutely nothing I can do about it. I don't want to be walking round with moth eaten looking hair and people commenting that I should just have my head shaved. It takes them a while and the pile of locks on the floor is huge. When they have finished I summon the courage to look. It isn't too bad, I think I am blessed with a head shape that can carry the bald look but I don't think I will be taking my hat off all that often. Chris's first comment is that I look like a lesbian! We laugh.

Day 7   *Hb 10.5 WCC 0.39 Neuts 0.17 Platelets 141*
Another long day and sleepless night are in store for me. I continue to think about what I do and do not want. I decide that I definitely want a scan sooner rather than later and that my decision making could be based on that. If the pictures are worse then I can justify walking away to both myself and the family. I gave it a go with treatment, it got worse, I'm going to enjoy the time I've got left without too much hospital intervention. If the scan shows improvement then I will be mentally stronger to face more chemotherapy. The in between result is harder to resolve in my mind. The palliative care Registrar pops by and I run through my thoughts with him. He thinks I am being rational.

Day 8   *Hb 10.0 WCC 0.87 Neuts 0.37 Platelets 215*
The constant thinking about what is the best thing to do is wearing me out. DtM is back today and my nurse is worried about me mentally so phones him and he promises to see me after clinic. When he eventually arrives I tell him I am a broken woman and that I do not know how much more of this I can face especially if there is not going to be a measurable response to treatment and all this suffering is pointless. I ask for a scan to help me and he thinks this is a reasonable idea. I definitely cannot face more chemotherapy on Monday as planned. I have only had eight days at home in six weeks and need a proper break from the hospital. He also agrees to this and suggests coming back to clinic in two weeks after the scan. The conversation brings an end to days of emotional turmoil and not for the first time I really appreciate his time.

Day 9   *Hb 11.3 WCC 2.11 Neuts 1.16 Platelets 427*
My bone marrow has finally woken up properly from its hibernation today and I make my escape for my two weeks of freedom.

Unexpected news

I go to this clinic appointment alone as Chris has missed enough work lately. The waiting room is quieter than the last time and I settle down in a chair with a good view of everything and read my book. I don't understand how Oncology clinics can end up running so late so quickly. My appointment is for 10.20am but it is after half eleven when DtM fetches me. It has been a lovely two weeks away from hospital and I am grateful that I have had the opportunity to fully recuperate before deciding about more treatment. We have managed to get out and about quite a bit, especially in the second week and until the last three days things have been going well on the symptom control front. Unfortunately though for the past few days night time back and pelvic pain have been an issue, I have started with PV bleeding again and have vomited a couple of times for no apparent reason. He examines me and clinically the pelvic mass is noticeably smaller and less tender. Whilst he is examining me he asks if I am sleeping and I admit to my insomnia.

Instead of telling me the MRI result he beckons me over to his computer screen and allows me read the report for myself. I am slightly taken aback as I read. Everything looks better, there is marked improvement in the lymphadenopathy and peritoneal disease, reduction in the size of the masses and improvement in the bone disease. The Radiologists do not make a comment about my liver so we look at the images and cannot identify the bright spots that were present on the previous scan. I sit down and sigh. I really was expecting the scan to show no improvement or worsening of the disease and being a natural pessimist I had rehearsed those scenarios in my mind more thoroughly. I was going to walk away from treatment and get to know the palliative care team better. I feel as though the carpet has been pulled from under me and the tables have turned completely. I don't think my reaction is quite what he was expecting. He thinks my symptoms for the past couple of days are best explained by 'tumour escape'. I remain quiet and stare at the floor. I think to myself if the tumour cells can 'escape' in only one month then what hope do I have and what is the point of any more treatment. I try and fight the tears. I decide to be brave and try to think logically; if there has been such a measurable response after relatively little chemotherapy then surely it is worth pursuing this a bit further even though it means subjecting myself to more suffering. Eventually I manage to verbalise this decision.

Today is the first time he mentions surgery although he is dubious that this would be the right option for me given the extent of my disease and I get the feeling he is only mentioning it because he knows I've read the papers and might bring it up anyway. He half heartedly offers to refer me for a second opinion. Although I had read about surgery being part of the Kushner P6 protocol I kind of assumed that in view of the metastatic disease that this would never be considered in my case. I'm not sure I want to have a big operation in the final months of my life anyway. I think he is pleased I share he scepticism on this topic, but says we can always revisit it at a later stage if I wish to pursue it. I promise myself to do some more research into surgery in DSRCT. As I leave to face more chemotherapy I really do feel that I am stuck between a rock and hard place. He gives me a hug.

85

Round two

There are no beds available on the day of clinic so I am given a day's reprieve. I am disappointed about this; I was all psyched up and ready to go after clinic. The following day I am admitted at lunchtime for the second cycle of high dose CAV. They give me the side room I was initially in and it feels quite nostalgic sitting in there waiting for the torture to begin. We have planned for me to have a Nozinan syringe driver and Lansoprazole from the start with the hope that these interventions will reduce my suffering this time. I am used to the routine now. The ward seems manic today and my nurse is new so I am glad when the two ward sisters arrive to give my chemotherapy. I remain impressed by the Oncology nurse's perfect aseptic technique when accessing my line. I have been cringing when the district nurse flushes my line as her aseptic technique is less than perfect, but I suppose it is more difficult in the community. I still do not feel able to take on this responsibility yet, but I might change my mind in the near future. However, if I were to get line sepsis I would be mortified.

After the identity check we crack on starting with the vincristine. Lying in a hospital bed hooked up to chemotherapy is the reality of my life at the moment and is pretty miserable, but I have properly thought about whether it is what I want to do and I think it is. I am not ready to start the long wait for death quite yet without at least putting up some fight. My thoughts about treatment have been circling round and round in my mind especially at night. When I was first diagnosed I was quite ambivalent towards treatment, but reading the evidence has confused the hell out me. Some patients even with advanced disease manage to survive in the medium term, which would mean I could achieve a little more with my life. It has taken me a while to realise it, but I am not ready to give up yet and I just need to be braver and face up to the chemotherapy with all my mental strength possible.

The first two days are so much easier with the Nozinan and I cannot believe how well I am tolerating it given my previous experiences. In addition to getting the symptomatic relief drugs right this time I suppose it is a little easier this time knowing that the chemotherapy is having a positive impact and causing tumour shrinkage. I even manage to eat a little. The Nozinan does make me very drowsy though, more so than last time. However I am so sleep deprived that catching up on some shut eye could only be a positive thing. The third day is more difficult with some retching and abdominal pain but I sit it out and it soon resolves. I am allowed home the following day and wonder if I will get septic this time.

An early birthday 'present'

Five days after my discharge I had been doing some cooking and suddenly start to feel unwell. I know exactly what is coming so lay down on the sofa and the rigoring soon sets in. My mouth is sore so I know I'm neutropaenic. Chris is much calmer this time. My temperature has risen from 36.1°C to 37.8°C in the space of a few minutes. Chris phones the hospital and they ask us to come in as soon as we can to the Teenage Cancer Unit as there are no beds on the assessment unit.

The ward is more like a hotel than a hospital. It is all decorated up for Halloween, a reminder that I will probably now be an in-patient for my thirtieth birthday. My side room is gorgeous; there is feature wall decorated with green and white swirls and a 32 inch flat screen television on the wall. Chris explores the bathroom and is surprised to discover the shower wall has a huge colourful mural of fish on it. I am feeling too ill to appreciate the surroundings though. The bed is comfier than the beds on my usual ward and I lie down.

My temperature is down to 37.4°C when they do my observations but I remain tachycardic. I am cultured from everywhere and the usual combination of fluids and Tazocin is prescribed. I settle down to try and rest. My neutrophil count is surprisingly high for me at 0.4 but I'm sure they will be on their way down soon enough. I feel washed out and rough. The on call Consultant sees me first thing in the morning, I haven't seen him before but he seems really nice. He has that sympathetic 'you're going to die soon' look in his eyes though. I am still feeling rough but my temperature is down and they agree the management plan. The morning bloods have shown a neutrophil count of 0.1 so they are falling quickly. He offers to discuss GCSF with my Consultant to see if we can shorten the neutropaenic period in time to get me out for my birthday. Unfortunately I am not really sick enough clinically for GCSF and my team say no.

I acquire a new problem this admission with my liver function tests. The Registrar comes to talk to me about it. I knew that my ALT had been up a little bit in the past and I had noticed it was 91 when I was admitted for chemotherapy but now it was over 400 and there was no good explanation for this. She thinks it could be drug related so my Tazocin and norethisterone are to be discontinued and they need to send a non-invasive liver screen. She tells me to try not to worry about it too much; it is probably just a blip because I am unwell. She is new to the team and doesn't know me very well yet, of course I'm going to worry, I've got a hepatitis without apparent cause. I ask about an ultrasound, this will happen after the weekend if there has been no improvement in my bloods.

I meet the other sarcoma Consultant on the Friday morning ward round. She seems nice and competent enough but I have built up a rapport and trust in DtM over the past few months and it doesn't seem right seeing someone else. I think I also get on better with men. I'm not entirely sure why but I always felt more comfortable working for a male boss. Female Consultants often seem to have a chip on their shoulders, although this is not true of this Consultant. One of my friend's husbands is an Interventional Radiology Consultant and has made a suggestion about metal ureteric stents as a means of losing the nephrostomies permanently. This is the first opportunity I have had to bring this up with my team so I

89

do. I am majorly disappointed with her reaction, she has no clinical experience of metal stents and envisages lots of problems, most of which I could counter-argue effectively but I choose not to. I do not know her well enough to have a fight yet. I guess she cannot ever really understand my desperation to be rid of the nephrostomies as she has never been in this situation herself. I will manipulate DtM into getting me the stents when I get the opportunity.

The weekend is long. I have some problems with non-specific abdominal pain and need a fair bit of Oxynorm. The on call Consultant is the same chap as earlier in the week and pops by to see me both days. I'm not that unwell and am sure that this isn't really necessary but it is reassuring. He informs me my neutrophil count remains flat; I even manage a record 0.00 on the Sunday. My platelets also drop to 10 and I need transfusing both platelets and packed cells. I am much less paranoid about the transfusion this time. The ALT continues to rise and is well over 500 now. I continue to feel washed out and depressed.

Ruined

I have been wide awake since 4am on the morning of my birthday. The box of tissues is rapidly running out. I have not had a good cry in a while. The fact I am still in hospital for the day is not really what is distressing me although it is not exactly how I had planned to celebrate my thirtieth. I just cannot stop thinking that I will probably not be having another birthday so what's the point. The nurses pop in one by one to wish me well which makes me cry even more, they have all even signed a card for me. The best birthday present would have been an increasing neutrophil count but unfortunately it remains at 0.02. The complimentary therapist is visiting the ward today and offers me some therapy so I opt for some reflexology which is a welcome and comforting surprise. I am getting quite into my complimentary therapies since becoming ill, they can't do any harm and relaxation is important when your body is under so much physiological stress. Chris visits in the afternoon with a Marks and Spencer's deli buffet that I can't eat because of my mouth and we open my cards and presents together. No champagne for me.

Grumpy

The day after my birthday DtM is back looking after the ward and does his Tuesday ward round. I am not in the best of moods. He had promised me less myelosuppression with this cycle which unfortunately has not been the case and I suppose I am just annoyed because I ended up spending my birthday in hospital. It's not his fault but I feel like blaming someone and he seems like the obvious choice. The liver issue is also worrying me. I have been following my blood tests closely and get the nurses to print them out for me daily. Having an ALT of over 500 probably wouldn't be much of a worry to the average patient but without a good explanation as to it's aetiology I am fretting about it constantly. Ignorance is sometimes bliss. He tries to explain it away as all due to the Tazocin. I am feeling a touch on the feisty side today and I am not about to be fobbed off so ask "why was my ALT 91 when I was admitted for chemo then?" This puts him on the back foot and he thinks aloud the other possibilities, the norethisterone is quite high on the list. It is less than ideal that this had to be stopped as I am now bleeding like a stuck pig. He then says it might have been due to the etoposide. I have to jog his memory that the last cycle was high dose CAV and that I have not actually had any etoposide yet. I remember that my ALT had been slightly abnormal on occasion before any chemotherapy or norethisterone and remind them of this fact too. The Registrar confirms I am right about this. The juniors stare at the floor. I know everything that has gone on with my illness and this knowledge is the one thing I can keep complete control of. He looks a bit deflated and says they will have to plot all my LFTs against clinical events to see if we can find any firm connections.

I tackle the issue of metal stents next. I have been keen to talk to him about it and am desperate to be rid of my nephrostomies as I have been living with them for over two months now; if one thing is ruining my quality of life at the moment it is their constant presence. Sometimes I think the medical staff see a nice normal renal function and therefore surmise that everything is fine and dandy. It's not and if they had to live with bilateral nephrostomies day in day out they would understand. I would give anything to be able to turn over in bed, to sleep on my side, to have a bath, to share a bed with my husband again and to be able to just go out of the house without worrying about either my leg bags slipping off or people staring at my drainage bags. Most people take these simple functions for granted, but when they are taken away life is truly miserable. In fact I have been so down about it I have thought on more than one occasion about removing the nephrostomies myself, taking a large dose of Oxynorm and letting nature take its course. If they think that I am not going to do my utmost to research alternative options then they don't know me very well. He seems more receptive to the idea than the other Consultant, but I can still sense some resistance. He admits to little experience of using them clinically but promises me he will do some research, discuss it with the Interventional Radiologists and we will talk again in clinic. I trust he will do these things for me.

Just to annoy me a little more he questions whether I have actually had neutropaenic sepsis at all this time as I have not had a temperature over 38°C. I can see his point to some extent but I was always taught to beware of the profoundly neutropaenic patients who do not mount a febrile response as they can end up a lot sicker due to delays in identifying and treating their sepsis. When I had pyelonephritis initially before I had been immunosuppressed, full blown rigors clinically, a CRP over 200 and a left kidney full of frank pus I never managed to get my temperature above 37.7°C. I just don't seem to mount a massive febrile response when I'm infected. I remind him of this. He asks if I am trying to talk myself out of a proposed discharge date in the morning provided there are no more fevers documented, I quickly shake my head and shut up. It is a slightly risky discharge as my CRP is gradually climbing and I am still profoundly neutropaenic, but I am not currently having any hospital interventions and they agree that if I am not sensible enough to come back if I feel unwell then who is. I escape as planned the following morning.

Making up

I've only had five days of freedom but I have really made the most of them and I'm feeling tired on Monday morning as I sit and wait in clinic. Apart from the jaded feeling though I am remarkably well. I have managed to wean off my Oxycontin dose completely which is a massive step forward and in my mind must equate to tumour shrinkage otherwise why would my analgesia requirements drop so significantly. As a result my mental clarity is back to usual and I just feel more normal. I have baked DtM my famous chocolate and raspberry brownies by means of an apology for being a grumpy, miserable cow on Tuesday. He receives the gift with humility and also apologises for messing up and not getting his facts straight before he saw me. I feel better we have made up; I didn't like falling out much.

He is keen to crack on with the next chemotherapy cycle whilst I remain up for it. It is time to alternate the agents so this cycle will consist of etoposide and ifosfamide. I have been doing my research on these drugs already. Etoposide is metabolised in the liver and can also cause abnormal liver biochemistry. I question what the plan is with my recent hepatitis in mind, he suggests 70% dosing to try and avoid toxicity but admits this is a judgement call and a bit of a guess. He explains about the encephalopathy that the ifosfamide can cause and that I have two of the three risk factors with my pelvic mass and renal problems. At first I think I might make a hilarious encephalopathic, I would obviously be very difficult and aggressive and need lots of sedation. On a more serious note though this news worries me, my mind is the one thing that is working well at the moment and without it I would not be me. I cannot help but think it would be interesting to experience an episode of acute delirium though. He explains there is an antidote if the craziness sets in, methylene blue.

He has researched the stent issue and is still a touch dubious that the metal stents are just a marketing ploy. He has however discussed it with the serious Radiologist who has agreed to give it a go. This news is music to my ears. It all comes flooding out about what living with nephrostomies is really like especially the sleep deprivation and I turn the water works on. I think he can see that I am ready to be without them if possible and promises to get the procedure organised for me as soon as is practically possible.

We talk about surgery next. I have joined an online forum for sufferers of DSRCT and lots of the members have been telling me surgery is a necessity no matter what the stage of disease. So I'd done some reading and there does seem to be a cohort of patients in whom surgery is a viable option and prolongs survival even in advanced disease. Although he feels I am not a surgical candidate he is receptive to my request to discuss my case with a surgeon and offers to refer me to a super specialist pelvic surgeon at the Christie in Manchester. This will happen after my next staging scan which seems sensible to me. As I leave clinic it feels as though we are back on the right track and I have achieved something with the stents and surgical referral. I feel quite content despite this awful illness and head off to face assassination attempt number three.

Hopeful pessimism

Cycle three is more tolerable than previous cycles. I don't know if it is the new drugs or just that I am becoming more experienced at receiving chemotherapy. I am not quite as well clinically towards the end of the cycle though and develop an impressive postural drop in blood pressure. It is rather disabling not having enough cerebral perfusion to be able to stand up for longer than a minute and I end up having to lie down on the bathroom floor on a mini mission just to brush my teeth. DtM thinks I am brewing an infection as I am also sweaty, tachycardic and have some new right iliac fossa tenderness, which delays my discharge. The promised infection does not however declare itself and I escape with a plan to return five days later for my stents. The encephalopathy does not occur, at last I have managed to avoid a complication.

I have been dubious about the timing of the stent procedure as it coincides with my neutropaenic period. I questioned this when the date was scheduled but was reassured it would be alright. DtM did agree to give me some GCSF, which I have been injecting religiously. The ward is really busy and for the first time I have to be in a bay. I have been very lucky to always have a side room for my previous admissions and I do not relish the thought of sharing other people's space. Hopefully it will only be a short admission and the excitement about the possibility of nephrostomy free living means that I am prepared to put up with a lot. I survey my room mates. The lady in the bed next to me is vomiting bilious fluid and clearly has a bowel obstruction. There is a woman in the bed in the corner who has an entourage of visitors, they are clearly not observing the two visitors per bed rule and it is not even visiting time yet. She does not appear unwell. The curtains are drawn around the other bed. Several of the Gynae-Oncology Consultants pop in and out with the serious grim reaper look on their faces so I guess the patient must be entering the terminal stage. Her husband cannot be any older than Chris. His eyes are blood shot. Luckily they move her to a side room later in the evening. I wonder if that will be me in a few months time.

It takes ages for the nurses to get round to taking my bloods as the ward is so manic. I feel very well and haven't got a sore mouth this time so am hopeful not to be neutropaenic. I venture out about midnight to discover my blood results and am pleased to find an SHO on my team sat at the nurse's station. I sit next to him and he checks the computer for me. As the results flash up I experience an awful sinking disappointed feeling. My neutrophil count is 0.1 despite the GCSF and my platelets are only 50. I am almost certain in my mind this equates to the procedure being cancelled and the SHO agrees. I guess I will have to wait a little longer for freedom from nephrostomies. I lie in bed staring at the ceiling for the rest of the night listening to the sound of others sleeping. I think the lady with the bowel obstruction must have aspirated, her chest sounds awful. As the hospital wakes up I text Chris with the bad news.

The sister phones Radiology and DtM with my blood results and to my great surprise they say to go ahead anyway. I am really not sure that it is the most sensible plan but as I was the one that had pushed for the stents in the first place feel I cannot dispute the decision. I get myself gowned up and ready to go. Soon I am on a trolley and I wonder if this will be the last time I have to manoeuvre with my nephrostomies. It is a long ride to the Vascular

Radiology department and I feel extremely nervous. I know the procedure is going to be painful and I am just hoping that I will be able to tolerate it and be brave.

The serious Radiologist waves at me as we arrive in the department but disappears again. They park me up in the recovery area and the nurse prepares me. She comments that I look petrified. One of the Radiology Registrars comes to introduce himself. He is rather handsome.
"As you are a special case I am losing out on my training opportunities this morning and the boss wants to do you himself."
All I can reply to this statement is "good."
We have a conversation about my illness and procedures so far and soon the Consultant reappears to consent me. As always I have read a great deal about the procedure and am well informed about the risks involved. I ask if he will be doing both sides and am pleased to hear he is hoping to achieve this. I am concerned though that he is planning to proceed without any sedation and see how I tolerate it as he wants me to be cooperative and able to move if necessary. I am however too scared to argue. I sign my life away to him again.

They wheel me through to the intervention room. It contains a mass of machines and screens, and I suspect would be a very scary environment to the non-medic. I transfer over to the table. They attach me to the monitors and the rapid beeping from the pulse oximeter confirms my anxious state. I roll onto my left side and try to get comfortable. The nurse takes my dressings down hopefully for what will be the last time. The fluoroscopy machine is positioned right above my abdomen and I feel a little claustrophobic. The Radiologist warns me about the cold chlorhexidine as he prepares the site. He is not very gentle and it really stings. "Are you ready for some local?" I answer in the affirmative and it is administered. I am getting so used to all these procedures now. As the contrast is injected into my ureter I flinch but I am well used to the feeling from previous nephrostograms. The long wire is inserted and he warns me as he pushes it through to my bladder. It feels very strange especially when he puts some contrast into my bladder. I desperately need to wee and have to concentrate hard not to. It must be quite a shock to my poor bladder after ten weeks of atony. The stent insertion itself is really quite painful but I hold the nurse's hand and take my mind off to the beach in Shetland. Soon it is over. He has left a tiny covering nephrostomy in situ but it is only a blind ending tube and can be removed after twenty four hours if my renal function and urine output are satisfactory. The tube is taped to my skin with a Tegaderm.

I roll onto my back and try to relax whilst they prepare for the other side. I already feel a little bit freer. I am so pleased they have managed to successfully stent one side at least and am glad that I pushed DtM to arrange the procedure for me. The Radiologist appears at my left side and asks how I'm doing. The scrub trolley contains masses of equipment. My illness is not being kind on the environment. Once they are ready I roll onto my right and the whole procedure is repeated. It is however much worse on the left side as he is trying to deploy the stent and I fail to maintain my quiet bravery. The poor nurse's hand must have been close to being broken and I am almost screaming. I beg for the drugs. He takes pity on me and orders the fentanyl and midazolam. I apologise for being a wuss and am told not to be silly. It takes what seems an age to get them ready and I wonder why on earth they don't have some already drawn up on standby. Finally they are administered and soon I feel myself floating and relaxing no longer caring what he is doing to me. He succeeds. I am shown the pictures and am impressed by them. The stents extend all the way from my renal pelvices to my bladder. Goodbye nephrostomies, hello to freedom.

For the first time in ten weeks I need to wee. They try to persuade me to use a bed pan because of the sedation but after my experience in America I want to use the toilet and I have come round completely now. The nurse insists on wheeling me to the loo. It is a very strange sensation as I pass urine, like a UTI magnified by ten but I am so grateful to be re-plumbed. Unsurprisingly I have haematuria. Moving around without the nephrostomies is also really weird but lovely, I feel like such a burden has been lifted. I thank the Radiologist as we leave, hopefully we will not be meeting again.

Told you so

I am excited to show the nurses my new found freedom as we arrive back on the ward and spin around on the spot for everyone to see. I feel genuinely happy for the first time in a long time. I need to wee frequently and it's really sore with bladder spasms but I don't care. It will settle and I'm prepared to put up with a lot for the freedom from those blasted drainage bags. I take a walk around the ward and am not quite sure what to do with my hands, they have had ten weeks of something to carry and now they have been liberated the possibilities are endless.

They do my post procedure observations and I come back down to earth with a bump. My temperature is 38°C and my pulse 139bpm. Soon I am feeling as rough as those observations would suggest and am confined to bed again. I knew this would happen, instrumentation of my renal tract whilst severely neutropaenic was not the cleverest idea and I feel vindicated that I had questioned whether to proceed. I am cultured and for the first time can actually provide an MSU as part of the sepsis work up. The Holy Grail that is Tazocin is given and we wait for my fever to settle. It is a long night. The urinary urgency is getting the better of me and I have several accidents. I am distraught about the incontinence, but the nurses are lovely and I give in to using pads. I wonder whether an anticholinergic might help, you can't take the doctor out of the patient even when I am unwell.

DtM pops his head round my drawn curtains the following morning. I am exhausted. He asks me whilst reaching for my folder "what does it show?" I am really not on top form today and cannot be bothered with his riddles so shrug. He meant my temperature chart and is pleased to see it is down this morning. He seems a little pessimistic about early stent infection causing major issues but I am really not in the mood for a fight or a debate and don't say much. I just need some sleep. I forget to ask about the anticholinergic. The next forty eight hours are difficult but then I turn a corner and things improve. Instead of needing to wee every fifteen minutes it is more like an hour after some serious concentrated effort on a bladder drill and I'm up and about again. My ability to bounce back clinically never fails to amaze me.

The nurses remove the covering nephrostomies under my guidance and for the first time I am completely tubeless, which in my mind signifies only one thing, bath-time! Having a bath was one of life's little luxuries that I used to really enjoy especially after a hard day at work. Not being able to have one through this illness has been killing me, I have never felt properly clean after a shower and even having a shower has not been a frequent event due to the nephrostomy dressings. I lock myself in the bathroom, fill the bath deep with hot water and bubbles and climb in. It is absolutely wonderful to be submerged in the water; all my muscles relax as well as my mind. I stay in for over an hour and look like a prune when I eventually drag myself out.

DtM sees me a few days later and I am a new woman. The bladder drill is working but I am still finding the bladder spasms very painful. I suggest the anticholinergic. I have already asked the SHO and the Registrar prior to this but no-one seems prepared to make a clinical decision about me without DtM's say so. Consequently even relatively minor decisions tend to get delayed and this is starting to annoy me. Continence is one of my specialist interests and

I suggest Solifenacin as my anticholinergic of choice in clinical practice as it is much more specific for muscarinic receptors in the bladder and therefore the systemic side effects such as blurred vision, dry mouth and constipation are much less prevalent. He has never heard of it but agrees to prescribe it if that is the one I would use. Mini battle won. It is home time later that day as I have completed my antibiotics and my neutrophils have recovered.

Reflective

I have managed for once to get an early clinic appointment this week and my friend Sarah has brought me so we can combine shopping and lunch before the unpleasantness of chemotherapy. I am determined to squeeze nice experiences into every last little bit of well time. DtM is still running twenty minutes late despite me having the second appointment of the morning. He waves at me in the waiting room, my cue to follow him into clinic. Sarah thinks he is odd but I like his eccentricity and am well used to it by now. The bag-less life has been suiting me well and I have managed to go back to work for a few days and Chris had taken me to Edinburgh for a luxury weekend away as a belated birthday celebration. I am also beginning to return to my previously active social life and hobbies. Good days are precious and I really make the most of mine. It is hard to think about more treatment making me feel rubbish again when I am so well at present, bloody Oncologists and their poisons.

My right iliac fossa remains tender on examination but I am pleased there is no renal angle tenderness. My abdomen however is unrecognisable compared to a few months ago and the pelvic mass is no longer palpable. DtM thinks the pain is tumour related and I agree, but I will not be going back to regular opiates, not yet anyway, my mental clarity is far too important. Paracetamol and the occasional Oxynorm will do me just fine. I admit to DtM about my recent preoccupation with death when he observes that I seem a little quiet. I have been thinking about death and dying a great deal recently, but I am not entirely sure why. Things are vastly improved compared with August, back then I didn't think I'd see Christmas and might have been pushing it to see my birthday and yet here I am now very much alive and kicking with improving disease and no nephrostomies. I am sill going to die though.

Death itself does not scare me; I came to terms with the fact that this illness is going to cut my life short many months ago. I do however have grave concerns about symptoms towards the end of life and in particular I am petrified about dying with a bowel obstruction. I have seen this happen to several patients before and in my opinion must be one of the worst ways to die with the most difficult to control symptomatology. I am worried about how Chris will cope when I die, he still has not completely accepted the fact that I will be dying in the relatively near future. He keeps saying that he doesn't want to go on if I do die, but I am not sure he is mentally strong enough to go through with suicide. At least he will be well supported when I do go. Being a control freak I have planned my funeral to the letter with music, poems, prayers, dress code and who I want to do what. DtM suggests a formal palliative care referral for me to discuss these thoughts further but I do not feel ready for this yet, I have only just started feeling properly alive again and I think I am just being silly given my recent massive improvement. He tries really hard to persuade me, but I stand firm and tell him I will be making the decision when I am ready for this. He gives up realising he is not going to win.

Round four

Cycle four is a relatively uneventful affair on the Teenage Unit as my usual ward is rammed although I suffer recurrence of the colicky abdominal pain I had experienced during cycle one. It soon settles with some opiates. I do however during my final nights stay develop some frank haematuria. I am obviously and understandably worried about haemorrhagic cystitis. I keep a sample to show the nurses. On my usual ward we had decided that dipstick positive haematuria that was not visible grossly was not a concern and that we would only take clinical action if the bleeding was frank. She reprimands me for not telling her before that I had 3+ blood on urinalysis, although if she had bothered to look on my fluid balance chart it is carefully documented with volume and macroscopic appearance since admission. I do not seem able to make her understand and give up. The doctor on call does not really speak English and I am sure he hasn't really understood either. He is discusses my case with the on call Registrar who also does not speak the best English and is a little 'hands off' in my opinion. He suggests intravenous fluids overnight. I know I should be having some more Mesna. My usual SHO sees me in the morning, discusses it with DtM and I finally get the Mesna. I hear on the grapevine DtM is a bit annoyed I didn't receive it in the night. The bleeding settles and I am allowed home.

I am hopeful that this time I may escape neutropaenic sepsis in the absence of the nephrostomies. Mum and Dad are recruited for neutropaenic babysitting duties whilst Chris works. It's fast approaching Christmas and he is starting to get really busy. I attend for an MRI scan on the Monday. I am a bit ambivalent about this scan, we know things are improving clinically and it is not going to change the management plan but I guess Oncologists like to see their poisons working as they go along. I get changed into the lovely hospital gown and psych myself up for the unpleasantness. The waiting room is full of snotty nosed children with various broken bones. In my day, you broke a bone, you got a cast, and it got better. These days it seems you have an MRI scan. The radiographer calls me through for a 'chat'. I immediately know they are not going to scan me. He says that the stents need to be in for six weeks before they can safely scan. I am annoyed as I had checked with both the serious Radiologist when he inserted them and DtM about the compatibility with MR as they are metal. I go home not in the best of moods.

They phone me from the MR department the following day to say it is actually safe to scan me as they have checked with the Medical Physics department. I am dubious. Me being me I have checked on the International MRI safety website and it definitely says to wait for six weeks. I have also read that the stents can heat up by as much as three degrees Celsius in ex vivo experiments. I re-attend for the scan. I have a routine for MRI scans now that makes the experience more bearable than the first time. I have an eye mask, my own music and take some lorazepam about thirty minutes before the scan. I am therefore quite chilled out lying on the table as they strap me in even with the doubts about safety. The scan is uneventful. It's a good job as my stents have rapidly become a very precious part of my life and freedom, and if something were to go wrong with them I would be devastated.

Misery

I make it to Thursday morning before my temperature spikes. I had persuaded Chris that babysitting was no longer necessary so I am alone. I hadn't felt brilliant in the morning so after my routine bubble bath had gone back to bed for a snooze. I then start to feel a bit warm. The thermometer tells me my temperature is 38.4°C. I try to ignore it, I really do not want to go back into hospital, I seem to spend most of my time there and this will mean another week of being uncomfortable. I know I am being irrational and that I could die if I don't phone but decide to leave it an hour like it says in the 'how to have cancer' guide. An hour later my temperature is still 38.3°C. Damn it. I phone the ward, the junior sister answers and organises me an ambulance. Five minutes later an ambulance responder knocks at my door. It is pouring with rain outside so we go in the kitchen as his boots are wet through and we've just had our carpets cleaned. He soon surmises I am a doctor although I do not readily volunteer the information. My pulse is 160 which seems to worry him a little. I remain pyrexial but my other observations are reasonable. The crew arrive soon after and whisk me away to Jimmy's with their blues and twos on full blast all the way. I am so sick of all this.

The usual routine follows on the Assessment Unit and within an hour I have been cultured from everywhere, had some Tazocin and the fluids are running. The Registrar who gave the bad advice regarding Mesna is on call. I am not all that impressed with his clinical skills. They have a side room on my usual ward and the junior sister has already earmarked it for me. They treat me well. Soon I am tucked up in bed. When my bloods eventually come back despite being marked urgent the pancytopaenia is impressive with a total white cell count of 0.02 and neutrophils of 0.01, platelets 10 and haemoglobin 7.5. No wonder I feel unwell. They organise yet more transfusions. I am trying to sleep when the on call Consultant comes to see me. I know his name by reputation but have never met him before. He is the typical Professor type. I cannot believe how many Professors there are in Oncology, it must be something to do with all the money from Cancer Research and the like sloshing about. My temperature is still up and I feel awful. He is very kind and sympathetic but nothing anyone says is going to make me feel better today. I am about as fed up as I can be. It would be so nice to just for once have chemotherapy without all these complications. One bit of positive news amongst all the doom and gloom though is that my MRI has shown some significant improvement.

Over the weekend I develop extreme anal pain when I open my bowels, which is a frequent occurrence as I am on Tazocin. It is so sore it is making me cry and is by far the worst pain I have experienced so far. Unfortunately all the doctors on call are men and even though I am seen both days by the Registrar I do not feel able to overcome my embarrassment and tell him. Chris has smuggled me in some Oxynorm from home which I have been taking more of than I should. My symptoms are worsening but luckily the nice female Registrar is doing a ward round on the Monday. I ask to speak in private and she examines me. I am still really embarrassed. It is so sore even just being inspected but luckily I am spared a PR exam in view of the neutropaenia. She finds an anal fissure and my peri-anal skin has broken down and is infected, all of which completely fits with my symptoms. Various creams are prescribed to try and soothe things. Why can't I just have a little peace? I don't remember signing up for all this when I agreed to chemo. I am truly miserable.

Bing Bing Bong

I cannot believe I have made it to cycle five. DtM is on annual leave today so I am seen in clinic by the female Consultant. Although she is very nice we still have little in the way of a rapport. I really do not have much to say, I'm here for my chemo, I still have incurable cancer, let's just get on with it without all the unnecessary chit chat. I'm in one of my 'what's the point' moods and have been contemplating whether my quality of life is what I need it to be at the moment. Once you embark on the chemotherapy path it's like a rollercoaster with very little opportunity to disembark. Life becomes ruled by this timetable of appointments and admissions, planning when sepsis is going to occur and when well days might be. She uses that Oncology speak "useful response to treatment". What does that mean exactly? They are not going to cure me, well I know that, but how can she determine what is useful to me? It's patronising. DtM does not use the usual Oncology language with me and has not broached timeframes yet, mainly I suspect because I never bring it up myself. I know we're talking months and I don't need a Consultant to tell me that.

I am having etoposide and ifosfamide this time. It consists of three litres of fluid given overnight for five days so my sleep is interrupted by the continued need to pass urine. I had just been getting back to normal and managing to sleep most the night without needing to wee. The incessant bing bing bong of the infusion pump is also really starting to grate on me. I sometimes hear it in my sleep when I am at home. There are different alarms for an occlusion below the pump, for low battery, for air in the cassette. I am starting to be able to recognise which is which without even looking at the machine.

They move me two days before the chemo is due to finish from my usual ward to the Teenage Unit. Winter bed crisis. I am put in the bay on the Unit. My room mates are a girl with recently diagnosed relapsed Hodgkin's disease and another lady with metastatic breast cancer. The girl with Hodgkin's is hard work. She is very needy and doesn't really understand how a hospital works especially how busy staff are. The breast cancer lady is having difficulty accepting the fact she is dying and is clinging on for every last little bit of treatment. I will not be like that. The emotional atmosphere in the bay is quite oppressive and I am very glad to be leaving when I finally finish my treatment on Christmas Eve. I flatter myself that perhaps I am dealing with the awfulness of my situation better than most.

Throwing in the towel

I have sat at home for two days with excruciating abdominal pain. I also have severe haematuria and am passing blood clots. My temperature is flicking up and down but is over the 38°C mark most of the day. I cannot bring myself to pick up the phone and just keep taking Oxynorm. Chris returns from work, takes one look at me and phones the hospital. I am being completely irrational and do not want to go. He takes me anyway.

A senior SHO who is about to take up an Oncology Registrar post clerks me in. I give my history. I am apprehensive about an abdominal exam as I am so sore but it has to be done. He notices the Muehrcke's lines I have developed on my finger nails since becoming ill. The left side of my abdomen is extremely painful even on the lightest palpation with rebound tenderness. My left side hurts when he percusses the right. Oh my god I have a peritonitic abdomen. He looks worried. I feel worried. He correctly thinks I need an urgent CT and surgical review, but will get the on call Registrar to see me. The nurses kindly drug me up.

The Registrar is a lovely Irish chap. I am subjected to another very uncomfortable abdominal exam and he has the same concerns as the SHO. It's getting late and I feel very guilty for being the reason he has had to remain at the hospital. He arranges the CT scan promptly and soon I am drinking the oral contrast. My bloods come back showing the usual impressively severe pancytopaenia. I get myself onto the porter's trolley but am still very sore even after the opiates. The ride is uncomfortable and the Registrar comes with me. I used to like to accompany my patients to scans, especially when I was doing Stroke. The

CT itself is rapid and uneventful. Soon I am tucked up in a bed on the Teenage Unit and drugged a little more. The Registrar comes by to see me. The scan hasn't shown anything drastic other than some slight stent migration on the left and some mild inflammatory changes. He has discussed me with DtM who happens to be on call and agreed an appropriate management plan. He checks I wish to remain DNAR which I do. I fail to sleep.

A Consultant friend is visiting when DtM turns up the next day with one of his new SHOs. He introduces himself to her without giving me the chance to do the introductions. They haven't met before, but I guess the worlds of Geriatrics and Oncology rarely collide. She leaves us to it. I am sleep deprived, in pain and depressed today so am really not in the mood for talking.
"I'm so fed up." DtM responds "I can see that."
My abdomen remains very tender and I remain pyrexial and sweaty. I am just going to have to sit it out; I have been here many times before. They do not stay long.

I have been weighing up the burdens of treatment versus the benefits for a number of cycles now and today I really feel the burden of lying in a hospital bed in excruciating pain is not worth the benefit the chemotherapy is giving me. I'm crying as I realise I have come to the decision to stop. It doesn't feel to me as though I am giving up as I have done my best and got much further with the treatment than I ever expected to, but I know that is how it will look to everyone else. I just want my old life back, even if that is just for a couple of months. I really cannot face feeling this ill another two times and who knows what horrible painful complication I will acquire next.

DtM pops his head round the curtain whilst I am sobbing. I had not expected to see him today as it is a Saturday and I am really not that unwell clinically to require a weekend Consultant review. I guess he must have sensed all was not well yesterday. "I think I might be done". He thinks I'm talking about this admission and I have to explain I mean with treatment altogether. We have a long chat and he reminds me we have been in this situation before at the end of cycle one. This is completely different though. Although I am upset, I feel quite peaceful inside about the decision to stop, it just feels like the right thing for me to do. I will not be changing my mind in the offered cooling off period. "Come back to clinic when you're ready".

I do not ask DtM to write me anymore chemotherapy prescriptions. So here my story ends. I now have to live what life I have left, complete my 'Bucket List' and get back to work for as long as is practical. It has been a horrendous convoluted journey but I have learned much about myself and many things that will make me a better doctor. Who knows how long I have but I am determined to remain cheerful, to enjoy life to the full and always to remember there is someone out there worse off than me.

Glossary

Acute kidney injury	Doctor speak for kidney failure
Adnexa	Where the ovaries and Fallopian tubes are located
Alfentanil	An injectable strong opiate medication used most commonly in patients with renal failure
ALT	A liver enzyme, blood levels go up in hepatitis
Anal fissure	A tear in the lining of the skin around the anus
Antecubital fossa	Where the skin creases at the elbow, the most common place used for taking blood samples
Anterior	Anatomical term for in front
Anticholinergic	A medication that blocks acetylcholine, which is is a type of neurotransmitter
Apyrexial	Without a fever
Arrhythmia	An abnormal rhythm of the heart
Atelectasis	Where part of the lung tissue, usually at the bases is not properly inflated
Atony	Refers to a muscle that has lost its strength
Bilateral	Both sides
Buccal mucosa	The lining of the mouth inside the cheeks
C. difficile	A type of bacteria that causes severe diarrhoea particularly in elderly and frail patients and those who have been treated with antibiotics
Calcium gluconate	An intravenous medication given to protect the heart from abnormal rhythms when the potassium level in the blood is too high
Cannulation	Insertion of a small plastic tube into a vein so that medication and fluids can be given intravenously
Catecholamines	Fancy name for adrenaline and other similar hormones
CAV	The abbreviation used for the combination of cyclophosphamide, doxorubicin and vincristine chemotherapy
Chlorhexidine	An antiseptic solution used to clean the skin before procedures
Circum-oral	Around the mouth
Creatinine	A blood test used to look at kidney function (usual range 60-100)
CRP	A blood test that measures inflammation in the body
CTPA	A CT scan used to look for pulmonary embolism
Cyclizine	An anti-sickness medication
Cyclophosphamide	A type of chemotherapy drug
Cytogenetics	The study of genetics on cell level, looking at abnormalities within chromosomes

Detrusor	The muscle of the bladder wall
Dexamethasone	A steroid medication, used to reduce inflammation and treat nausea associated with chemotherapy
Distal ureter	The end of the ureter just before it enters the bladder
Diuresis	Production of urine
DNAR	Do not attempt resuscitation
Doxorubicin	A type of chemotherapy drug
DVT	Deep vein thrombosis, a blood clot usually in the veins of the legs
Dysuria	Stinging pain when you pass water
ECG	A tracing of the electrical activity of the heart
EMLA cream	A local anaesthetic cream
Encephalopathy	Disease or disorder of the brain
Etoposide	A type of chemotherapy drug
Extrinsic compression	Compression from something outside an organ e.g. a tumour
Fentanyl	A type of strong opiate used for pain relief
Flexible cystoscopy	A camera test used to look at the lining of the bladder
Fluoroscopy	An X-ray test where real time images are taken and viewed on a screen
GCSF	An injected medicine can boost the neutrophil count, usually given after chemotherapy
Germ cell tumour	A cancer arising from germ cells, which are specialised cells found in the ovary or testis
Haematoma	A collection of blood outside a blood vessel
Haemorrhagic cystitis	Inflammation of the lining of the bladder causing bleeding and pain, usually a result of cyclophosphamide or ifosfamide treatment
Hb	Abbreviation for haemoglobin, the oxygen carrying molecule in the blood (normal range 11.5-13.5 for a woman)
HCA	Healthcare Assistant, an untrained member of staff who support nurses in their role
Heterogeneous	Different (textures)
Hickman line	An intravenous line inserted into a neck vein and most commonly used to administer chemotherapy
Histopathologist	A doctor who specialises in diagnosing conditions by looking at biopsies
Hydronephrosis	When the kidneys are swollen, usually due to an obstruction in the ureters or bladder
Hypertension	High blood pressure
Ifosfamide	A type of chemotherapy drug

Iliac fossa	The lower part of the abdomen either side of the midline
Immunohistochemistry	Using specific antibodies to detect certain proteins on cell surfaces, mainly used in the diagnosis of cancers
Instillagel	A local anaesthetic gel, most commonly used when inserting a catheter or prior to cystoscopy
IPCC	Intermittent pneumatic calf compression, a mechanical device which inflates and deflates sleeves around the calf muscles to prevent blood clots
Klebsiella	A type of bacteria that causes serious infection
Lansoprazole	A type of proton pump inhibitor, a medication that reduces acid production in the stomach
Laparotomy	A big abdominal operation
Levomepromazine	Also known by trade name Nozinan, an anti-sickness drug
Lignocaine	A local anaesthetic
LMWH	Low molecular weight heparin, a type of blood thinning medication that is used to prevent blood clots
Lorazepam	A type of short acting benzodiazepine medication used to treat anxiety
Lymphadenopathy	Enlarged lymph nodes, most commonly due to infections or cancer
MDT	Multidisciplinary Team, in cancer care this consists of Surgeons, Oncologists, Radiologists, Histopathologists and specialists nurses
Meropenem	An intravenous antibioitic used in severe infections
Mesna	A medication used to prevent haemorrghagic cystitis in patients on cyclophosphamide or ifosfamide
Metastases	When a cancer spreads to a distant organ from the original tumour
Methylene blue	A blue dye that is given intravenously to prevent and treat ifosfamide induced encephalopathy
Midazolam	A sedative medication that belongs to the group of medicines called benzodiazepines
MSU	Medical speak for a clean catch urine specimen
Mucosa	The inner lining of an organ
Muehrcke's lines	Horizontal white lines on the fingernails, usually as a consequence of illness
Muscarinic receptor	A type of receptor that acetylcholine acts on
Myelosuppression	When the bone marrow is not working properly, most commonly as a result of chemotherapy, infections or cancer

Nephron	The building block of a kidney, performs filtration of the blood
Nephrostogram	An examination where a dye is injected into a nephrostomy and X-rays taken to see if there are any blockages/kinks
Nephrostomy	A tube inserted directly into the kidney through the skin to relieve an obstruction in the ureter
Neutropaenia	A low neutrophil count (normal range 2-11)
Neutropaenic sepsis	An infection when the neutrophil count is low
Neutrophils	The most common type of white blood cell
Norethisterone	A medication given to stop periods
Obstructive uropathy	When the kidneys fail due back pressure caused by an obstruction somewhere in the renal tract
Omentum	A fold of peritoneum, which is the lining of the abdominal cavity
Ondansetron	An anti-sickness (anti-emetic) medicine
Opiates	Medicines such as morphine which act on opioid receptors in the body to give pain relief
Oramorph	A liquid form of short acting morphine
Oxycontin	A type of strong long acting opiate medicine
Oxynorm	A type of strong fast acting opiate medicine
PACES	An practical exam doctors have to pass to become a Member of the Royal College of Physicians
Pancreatitis	Inflammation of the pancreas
Pancytopaenia	When all the blood counts are low (haemoglobin, white cells and platelets)
Pat-slide	A large stiff plastic board used to transfer patients between beds
PE	Pulmonary embolism, a blood clot in the lung
Percutaneous	Through the skin
Peritonitis	Inflammation in the peritoneum, the lining of the abdominal cavity
Pharmacology	The study of the action of drugs
Pleural effusion	Collection of fluid around the lung
Plts	Abbreviation for platelet count, fragmented cells in the blood involved in helping the blood to clot
Pneumothorax	A collapsed lung
Polyuria	Passing loads of urine
Posterior	Medical term for behind
Potassium	A salt in the blood, normal level 3.5-5
PPI	'Proton Pump Inhibitor', a medication used to stop acid production in the stomach and relieve indigestion and gastritis type symptoms
PR exam	Doctor speak for a rectal examination
Pre-syncope	That feeling just before you faint

Propofol	A drug commonly used for general anaesthesia
PV bleeding	Bleeding vaginally
Pyelonephritis	An infection of the kidney
Refeeding syndrome	A rare condition that occurs when someone has been starved then starts to eat again
Renal parenchyma	The bulk of the kidney where the filtration occurs
Renal pelvis	The central part of a kidney where the ureters begin and urine drains into
Rifampicin	A type of antibiotic that turns your urine orange
Rigor	A shivering do usually caused by an infection
Sacrum	The lower part of the spine where the pelvis attaches
Seldinger chest drain	A tube inserted into the chest wall using needles, wires and dilators to drain either air or fluid from around the lung
SHO/FY2	Abbreviations given to junior doctors
Solifenacin	An anticholinergic medication used to treat overactive bladder
Somatisation	When psychological distress manifests itself as physical symptoms
Stage 3c ovarian cancer	An advanced stage of ovarian cancer where the cancer has spread to abdominal lymph nodes and lining of the abdomen
Subclavian vein	A large vein found under the collar bone that drains blood into the heart
Suprapubic	The lower central part of the abdomen
Sympathetic overdrive	When the body's fight or flight response is activated mediated by adrenaline
Syringe driver	An infusion pump that delivers a medication subcutaneously (under the skin) over a twenty four hour period
Tachycardia	Rapid heart rate
Tachypnoea	Breathing quickly
Tazocin	A penicillin based antibiotic given intravenously
Tegaderm	A see-through dressing commonly used to secure an intravenous cannula
Thrombocytopaenia	A low platelet count (normal range 150-400)
Tinzaparin	A type of low molecular weight heparin
Tranexamic acid	A medication used to stop bleeding
TTO	'To Take Out', the abbreviation given to medication given to a patient when they are discharged from hospital
U+Es	Abbreviation for the blood test that looks at the salt levels and kidney function

Ureteric stents	Tubes inserted into the ureters to relieve a blockage. This can be retrograde i.e. from the bladder via a camera called a cytoscope or antegrade i.e. from the kidney down the way
Venepuncture	Fancy name for taking blood samples
Venous thromboembolism	Blood clots that form in veins in one part of the body, break off and travel to another organ, refers to DVT and PE
Vincristine	A type of chemotherapy drug
VTS	'Vocational Training Scheme', the name given to the training programme for GPs
WCC	Abbreviation for white cell count

Biography

Dr Kate Granger is a third year Elderly Medicine Registrar working at Pinderfields Hospital in West Yorkshire. She wrote this book during long sleepless nights whilst undergoing intensive chemotherapy for a rare, aggressive type of sarcoma. Kate is originally from Huddersfield but now lives in Wakefield with her husband Chris. She was inspired to write by one of her bosses, Dr Frank Phelan, who is a Consultant Physician at Pinderfields, suggested that she keep a diary about her experience of illness.